Montagu Barker was a brilliant Christiar
regretted that he did not publish more. The
his best papers is thus very much to be welcomed.

Jim Packer, Professor of Theology Regent College Vancouver

Monty Barker was an outstanding Christian psychiatrist who was in great demand not only for his medical expertise but for his lectures on pastoral care and counselling in theological colleges in the United Kingdom, France and India. I was particularly struck by his practical and selfless care of many clergy undergoing stress. This is a welcome collection of some of his writings and lectures which are still highly relevant today.

Michael Green, Senior Research Fellow Wycliffe Hall Oxford

Psychiatry has been a turbulent discipline for faint-hearted Christian medics. Yet Monty Barker navigated a channel through the cross-currents, which attracted many to follow in his wake. The warmth of his friendship, the breadth of his reading and the incisiveness of his thought drew many alongside him. In public lectures on pastoral care, he would illustrate his teaching from past heroes of the faith. His analysis of their problems, with his deep human sympathy and wry Scottish humour, always gripped his audiences, as I am sure this volume will do for its readers.

Peter May, Retired GP and Former Chairman
Universities and Colleges Christian Fellowship

As one of the many whom Monty Barker mentored, I am most grateful to have received the benefit of his breadth of interests, his depth of expertise, and his inimitable qualities of mind, personality and faith. This collection of his writings captures and expresses this for a wider readership not already familiar with his life, teaching and friendship. His characteristic forthright and incisive observations, always with a measure of grace and wit, continue to speak wisdom to different audiences of professionals in health and psychiatry, Christian leaders and teachers, and those with an interest in the intersection of faith, mental health and world mission.

Richard Harvey, Senior Researcher Jews for Jesus

I was a 24 year old student worker when Monty rather disturbingly told me at the door of Christ Church Clifton, 'You will need to see me in your late 30's, you'll be fine until then'. With that warning, and almost exactly 15 years later, time spent with Monty saved my future marriage and my ministry. I owe him an incalculable debt and am delighted to commend this volume to a new generation.

Rico Tice, Senior Minister (Evangelism)
All Souls Langham Place London

I have carried the profound theological and psychological insights of Monty Barker's teaching since my student days in Bristol in the 1970s. For many years these were in hard copy: tightly scribbled notes that tried to get down as much wisdom as my pen could capture. Those notes moved around the country with me, popping up in various guises in sermons, pastoral care workshops and finally in Cranmer Hall lectures and tutorials. But by then the notes were redundant because I had internalised Monty's teaching. Which is perhaps as well since somewhere between vicarages my old notes got lost... I am delighted that now, when asked where I learned such life knowledge, I can recommend a text to resource a new generation of Christian ministers.

Helen Thorp, Diocese of Durham
and Cranmer Hall Theological College.

I first benefited from the writing of Monty Barker when I was a student. Later on he became a wise friend, advisor and counsellor for me as he was to so many. His writings reveal his unique perspective which combined deep Biblical and theological understanding, broad clinical experience in psychiatry, providing pastoral support and advice for generations of Christian leaders and cross-cultural missionaries, and shrewd, perceptive and insightful observations of human nature. I'm delighted that this collection of his writings is being published.

John Wyatt, Emeritus Professor of Ethics and Perinatology,
University College London and President of the
Christian Medical Fellowship

From the Psychiatrist's Chair

Reflections on Health in the Family, in the
Workplace and in the Worldwide Church

From the Psychiatrist's Chair

Reflections on Health in the Family, in the Workplace and in the Worldwide Church

Selected Works of
Dr Monty Barker

MB ChB (cum laude) FRCPE FRCPsych DPM FRSA

Edited by Rosemary Barker, David Cranston and Daphne Key

CONTENTS

ACKNOWLEDGEMENTS

My son, more than the calf wishes to suck
does the cow yearn to suckle.

This quotation from Rabbi Akiba (in Roman captivity in the first century AD) to his favourite pupil, Simeon ben Yochai expresses well what drove my husband to continue teaching into his eighties. The fact that most of his teaching remained unpublished lies behind Professor David Cranston's resolve to preserve some of my husband's lectures from over the years and without him this book would certainly never have come into being, so to him my warm thanks.

The initial task was huge, deciphering sheets of scribbled notes, and David was helped in the transcription by several of the community of the Oxford Centre for Mission Studies. John Butler gave many hours in the early stages of the project, helping to select the contents. Peter May, one wonderful week in the Lake District, read through the whole manuscript and gave it his approval. Rico Tice and Richard Harvey have been unstinting in their enthusiasm and practical support. Daphne Key joined us at a critical moment, and gave many hours of her time and the gift of her meticulous editing skills without which we would never have achieved a manuscript worthy of publication. Lastly thanks go to Tony Gray our publisher who first gave the go-ahead for this book, so kick-starting it, and has not wavered in his support.

FOREWORD

In the early 1950s, just as the Christian Union at St Andrews University was expected to die out, 'from the ashes, like a phoenix, arose Monty Barker'. So reports Geraint Fielder in his book on the history of the Christian Union movement. This was not the only occasion when Monty's contribution to life went against the grain of people's expectations.

Applicants to medical school were expected to have studied the sciences: Monty had done classics. People who failed their first year university examinations so dismally were not expected to shine: Monty went on to graduate with honours. People who contracted tuberculous meningitis affecting the lining of the brain were not expected to live, let alone to graduate: Monty saw his 81st birthday.

This unusually intelligent young medical student, who was so important in leading the Christian Union at St Andrew's into growth, could have been expected to pursue a prestigious career as a physician. Against expectations he chose psychiatry, which then, as now, was neither a popular nor a particularly prestigious specialty.

Moreover he was entering dubious territory for Christians who believed that the Bible was the Word of God and it was an area into which few evangelicals had ventured. So along with a few others, Monty pioneered a path followed by a generation of Christian doctors now doing the same thing. Many, like myself, freshly out of medical school, came to Bristol to work with Monty Barker.

They say be careful what you pray for. And if you prayed to see a *Christian* psychiatrist and saw Monty Barker, you did not always get what you expected. Given the popular image of gentle Jesus meek and mild, Monty could sometimes be quite fierce, an intimidating teacher, plain speaking and no-nonsense. A young man whom Monty had helped enormously to get his life back on track told me what a huge difference Monty had made in his life. But 'boy', he said, 'he can't half put the boot in'.

So, if you went to see Monty Barker as his patient, or worked for him as a junior doctor, sometimes you needed to be prepared for the unexpected. As a friend and mentor too he was not afraid to say what he thought. But his counsel was all the better for his realism. His refusal to flatter meant that his encouragement felt solid and reliable. His friendship felt real and faithful and likely to endure. And his realism about some of his own struggles drew him alongside others who found it hard to make their way in life and they felt encouraged. His career also went against expectations. It did not in the end take the academic route of university researcher or professor of a department. Instead he devoted his extraordinary intellect and annoyingly accurate memory to exploring the questions that faith posed for psychiatry and that psychiatry posed to faith. The selection of his writings republished here is testimony to that. And still today, when I go to Christian conferences in the UK or internationally, say you come from Bristol and somebody will ask, 'Ah, you must know Monty Barker?'

And lastly when he got older, expected like so many others to slow down, to get set in his ways and become resistant to change, Monty went against the grain there as well. He found himself in his 'retirement' spending months each year right up until his death, enjoying a new career teaching in a theological college in India.

Of course like all of us, he struggled with bits of himself up until the end. He could sometimes be overly critical. If his wife, Rosemary, unwisely slipped out of the room when Monty and I got together, the world could soon be going to the dogs. But when she came back in it stopped. She always strove to bring out the better side of him and right up until the end that was what he wanted: to do better, to be better, to be forgiven. To have another opportunity to make a difference in the Kingdom of God.

Glynn Harrison, Professor Emeritus of Psychiatry,
University of Bristol

INTRODUCTION
Rosemary Barker

This book is a collection of talks and papers, most of them previously unpublished, that my husband gave over a period of many years. They cover a range of subjects that can be best described under the general heading of the health of the family and the church. As some were written many years ago, a few of the phrases and illustrations may be dated, but the issues and the subjects that they cover are as relevant today as in the past and our hope and prayer is that this book will continue to help and benefit the Christian community for many years to come.

Issues in the Family
Making a Good Marriage, Making Good Parents and *Enjoying the Teen Years* are the titles of a series of lectures given at a Family Service Seminar at Christ Church Clifton in Bristol during the 1980s. They were repeated by popular request in 1992 and many times since in different contexts. The theme of mutual caring is explored, and clearly touched a nerve for many, not least for Monty's students in India since over the years he was invited to preach at weddings all over India, from Nagaland in the north-east to Tamil Nadu in the far south. And his marriage preparation was legendary.

Issues of Health
The chapter on *Sleeplessness* arose out of an invitation to preach at Christ Church on Psalm 4, which Monty called 'the Psalm for insomniacs'! Here insights from Scripture and from psychology

are brought together – the focus being to help the person in the pew as well as the patient in the clinic.

The same could be said of the chapter entitled *Bereavement*. It was while discussing this topic back in the late 1980s that an invitation came to teach at Union Biblical Seminary in Pune, India where as in many societies there was very little teaching in the churches that brought together the need to grieve a loss along with the healing power for the believer of hope in Christ's resurrection. The topic became a key element of a course in Pastoral Studies given at UBS each year for 25 years, and of similar courses at Trinity College, Bristol and the Faculté Libre de Théologie Evangélique at Vaux-sur-Seine near Paris.

Depression was perhaps the topic most often requested among lay audiences, and here different models for understanding depression are offered, along with practical advice regarding treatment and help.

The chapter on *Demon Possession and the Occult* will not satisfy everyone, but grew out of the experience of treating a number of young patients admitted to psychiatric hospital. A pattern emerged from their histories, and with the current tragic stories of young people suffering from the accusation of being possessed, and recent headlines such as 'Toddler dies of hunger in commune exorcism', the editors decided the material here, though dated, was important enough to be included.

Issues in the workplace
In the belief that prevention is better than cure, these three papers on *Conflicting Demands of Work and Family*, *Master or Slave of Time* and *Avoiding Burnout* are hard-hitting. In fact, the first paper caused quite a stir when it was given at the annual meeting of the Association of Surgeons of Great Britain and Ireland in 1994, prompting a number of phone calls to be made, and flowers to be sent as soon as the meeting ended! The papers grew out of many hours listening to friends and patients tell their story, and they attempt to give to as many as possible the insight and the tools they need to avoid breakdown.

Issues in the Pastoral Ministry

The topics dealt with here were increasingly in demand in churches and clergy conferences in the late 1990s as 'care for the carers' became a growing concern, as did the number of Christian workers needing help and counselling. *The Call to the Ministry* examines those hidden motives that, while not in any way negating the reality of God's call of a person to ministry, need to be looked at, recognised and brought out into the open in order to prevent breakdown later on.

The Minister's Expectations of their Ministry again calls for an honest look at psychological aspects of our personalities that otherwise may trip us up when we face difficulties or disappointments.

The Minister and the Fellowship suggests two very different models or mindsets between those who see themselves as leaders in their churches and those who see themselves as servants. The pitfalls of both are stressed, and instead the concept of the minister as a member of the fellowship is put forward. The close friendships of our Lord and his vulnerability to the disciples are suggested as a challenging but Biblical model for the minister in his relationship with the fellowship.

Issues in Cross-Cultural Mission

Dr Brainerd Prince, an alumnus of Union Biblical Seminary in Pune, India introduces this section with a paper given at the Oxford Centre for Mission Studies in March 2016. In *Mission as Polyhabiting Plural Worlds* he seeks to analyse the reasons for the success of Dr Barker as he sees it in entering genuinely into the culture and mindset of Indian society while in no way losing his Scottish identity.

The following two chapters are included by permission of Union Biblical Seminary where Monty and I taught as adjunct faculty for many years until his death in 2015. The first paper, *Counselling in an Indian Context*, appeared in August 1998 in a volume of essays in honour of Dr I Ben Wati, a highly respected Indian Christian leader and a close friend. He was one of the architects of UBS, on the Board for 32 years and its Chairman for 16, serving as Principal of the Seminary from 1994–1995. The paper seeks to fill a perceived gap by providing Indian-sourced reflections on Pastoral Care and Counselling as opposed to Western models. It ends with a plea 'for the training and on-going support of pastors and church leaders' throughout the Indian sub-continent.

Madness: the Cost of Mission? is a paper given at Union Biblical Seminary (UBS) in 2003 during the annual Centre for Mission Studies Consultation under the general title Leadership and Mission. The paper highlights the cost to William Carey's wife, Dorothy, of his remarkable missionary career in India, and urges those in mission oversight to be aware of the needs of the families of their workers.

The remaining four papers grew out of many, often informal, conversations with weary and even defeated missionaries. Help was also sought from my husband by sending agencies that wanted to give better care to their candidates and returning mission partners. All four papers seek to look honestly at the psychological aspects of personality that need to be recognised and built into the way a mission partner is assessed (*The Missionary Call*), deployed (*Psychological Aspects in Missionary Relationships*), cared for when they move between cultures (*Culture Shock and Counter Culture Shock*) and welcomed when they return home (*The Role of Mission Boards*). One newly returned mission partner described the content of these papers as challenging but immensely releasing, which we hope will be true of all the contents of this small volume.

ISSUES IN THE FAMILY

Chapter One
MAKING A GOOD MARRIAGE

O ne psychiatrist, on reviewing the mental health of couples, said, 'Marriage is good for men and bad for women!' There is good evidence that marriage protects men from psychiatric morbidity but it has the opposite effect on women. Women who are married have a four-fold incidence of being nervous, depressed and anxious, whereas men who are married have only half the incidence of their single colleagues. It has been suggested that there should be a government health warning for married women! However, it should be noted that the majority of married women are not psychiatrically ill and it does not mean that marriage is invariably a source of conflict and ill health.

In the 1950s, marital problems were thought to have nothing to do with psychiatry, and as a medical student I was taught that if someone came with marital problems, it would be best if they went to see a priest or a marriage counsellor. Ten years later in the 1960s there was a culture change, as a lot of psychological and sociological studies began looking at marriage and family issues. Professor Carstairs, a psychiatrist in Edinburgh, wrote a book that was the subject of his Reith lectures, entitled *This Island Now*, in which he identified the family as a source of guilt and other relational issues in the personal lives of married people. R D Laing, in both his book *The Divided Self* and a film, *Family Life*, expressed the view that families were bad for you and this influenced many medical students and other young people of that era. David Cooper, a psychologist at the same time, wrote a book entitled *The Death of the Family* in which he said the family

1

was the most perfected form of non-communication in our culture, and could be very destructive.

Move forward then to the 1970s, sometimes called the 'me' decade. Here the talk was about my fulfilment, my freedom, what I want. Marriage, it appeared, was becoming obsolete and the family seemed to be in decline. Everyone was 'doing his or her own thing'. There was an increase in abortion, divorce, co-habitation and 'serial monogamy', a term that appeared quite respectable on the surface with only one wife or husband at any one time but then a change for another.

Serial monogamy arose partly out of the fact that people were living longer, having good health longer and having smaller families. By the time one reached 40 there was a sense in which one was able to say, 'Gracious, I'm still a young person; where are we going in life?' Husband and wife looked at each other and thought, 'Why did I marry you? I think it's time we cut and run and had a go with somebody else.' In other words, one spouse was there for bringing up children and another spouse for later on in life after the children had left the nest.

Then in the 1980s people began to count the cost. Marriage breakdown was costing the country billions of pounds in social security, legal fees and other aspects. Psychologically too, it was found to have taken its toll. Suicide was shown to be 20 times greater among people of the same age who had just broken up, whether from marriage or any other close relationship. Alcoholism, heart disease and accidents were also all greater in people who had a broken relationship. Many accidents occur when somebody has had a real fight, a row or a split; one partner drives off in fury and then ends up in the local hospital or mortuary!

The next decade saw increasing concern for family life in such organisations as the World Health Organization and the World Council of Churches. 'The Year of the Family' was inaugurated, with slogans such as 'Families for Tomorrow', at which HRH Princess Diana gave a very moving introductory speech. With the passing of the Children's Act the government sought to set out a policy for family life. Slogans such as 'Single Parents – Double Trouble' began to be enunciated by the very people who were the pioneers of the feminist movement in the United States in the 1960s.

Since then the wheel has turned, and the question is being asked, 'What should one be aiming for in marriage?' There is a realisation that even if a third of marriages do break up, two-thirds do not. Even if there are two million children who are brought up with those who are not the genetic parents, there are nine million children who are still living with the parents responsible for their existence. In the 1960s and 1970s people were asking, 'What makes a bad marriage?' Now in the 1980s and 1990s people were asking, 'What makes a success in a marriage; why is it that some marriages actually stick?' This is in contrast to the 1960s when many people thought that the institution of marriage was going to disappear.

Robin Skynner wrote a book with John Cleese entitled *Families and How to Survive Them*. Skinner was a psychiatrist who discussed many family problems with Cleese. In an article in 1987, Skinner gave what he considered the life plan for marriages that do survive and his points were as follows:

First, the marriages that survive are of couples that accept the world as it is. There is realism in their approach to the world, to themselves and to their partners. They do not go chasing an illusive dream.

Second, they have positive social attitudes: these are people who are able to make friends. How does one choose a spouse? Ask if the person is able to make friends of their own sex. Do they have a genuinely positive attitude to other people?

Third, there is a respect for the other person's individuality. Instead of going into the relationship saying, 'I'll change him' or 'I'll change her' (it's usually the woman saying 'I'll change him'), it is rather acknowledging that the other person is an individual in their own right. Differences should be encouraged rather than squashed and the distinctive qualities of the person one has married should be recognised.

Fourth, there should be common values and goals. I often ask couples, 'What makes life tick for you'? Men often say 'my job', and the women often say 'my children'. The house may come next and if they mention each other at all it often comes later. What is most important in life is a common goal for which both are striving, and which is acknowledged as part and parcel of what a life together means. That is a life that is likely to withstand what Shakespeare called the 'slings and arrows of outrageous fortune'.

Fifth, effective communication with each other. When this takes place each knows what the other person thinks – or at least part of what the other person thinks. Then there is a chance of talking together and getting on together. It means being able to create a sense of fun between each other. Not just having fun and going out to parties, but the ability to laugh at oneself and be teased. A sense of humour can often see a couple through stormy occasions.

Sixth, space: but space within the closeness. Lady Coggan, wife of a former Archbishop of Canterbury, quoting Khalil Gibran, used to say 'let there be space in your togetherness'. The different activities and interests of each are acknowledged, enhanced and brought into the relationship. Skinner went on to say that people who can change, who can tolerate faults, people who can be teased and stand emotional discomfort and suchlike teething problems, are people who enter life as a learning experience and their marriages are likely to succeed.

Anthony Clare, the television psychiatrist, quoting Rollo May, wrote of people involved in serial monogamy with one relationship after another: 'They never really loved anyone long enough to get beyond the superficial problems which are here today and gone tomorrow.' Loving a husband or wife is a task a couple should be engaged in throughout their lives together.

In the Old Testament there is a story of a marriage in trouble, the marriage of Elkanah and Hannah. Elkanah was a man who had two wives. One of them, Hannah, did not have children and the other wife, Peninnah, did and she used to goad Hannah saying,

'You don't have any children, you're not much of a woman, are you?' Hannah used to get very uptight and her husband used to see this. He was aware that childlessness was looked upon not only as a disappointment but also as a disgrace in his society, so he used to give a double portion of food to Hannah as a means of compensation. But Hannah still wept and looked miserable and Elkanah would ask, 'Hannah, why are you so sad? Don't I mean more to you than lots of children?' Then one day she went to the temple and as she was pouring out her heart to God, Eli the old priest saw her and thought that she was drunk! She assured him that she was not drunk, and told her story to Eli. In a way he was like a marriage guidance counsellor – certainly he was a 'third party' who gave her some advice and off she went home, became pregnant, had a child whom she named Samuel and dedicated him to the service of God. She brought up the child for a few years and then handed him to Eli and the temple authorities to bring up as someone who would be trained to be a prophet.

Here we begin to have some idea of the Biblical view of how to deal with marriages that get into trouble, and it incorporates some of the things that Skynner elicited from his couples. It teaches that for a marriage to work well one needs to have honest and open communication; there needs to be a feeling of being heard. Not just talking, but knowing that what is being said is being listened to.

Sometimes if I have been very busy, I come home and my wife and I have a meal together and we chat about things and catch up with the day. On other occasions I am busy writing or reading and my wife will be talking about something, and then she suddenly stops. I look up and, putting my finger on the word that I've reached, I say, 'Yes, carry on.' She says, 'Oh, I've got eye contact at last, have I?' The point being made is that we think we are paying attention, and maybe we are paying attention, but we don't communicate that to the other person. So, communication has to be open and honest and give a feeling of being heard.

I sometimes give a little exercise to those who are married. I ask them to look at each other for five seconds – not say anything, just look at each other. I want them to ask themselves, 'Why did you marry that person? What made you look twice in that direction rather than another direction? What made you turn your head twice and then decide to go on with pursuing that relationship? Was it good looks, sexual attraction, plenty of money, good prospects, someone that you thought would need your help or someone to whom you would give your help? Maybe it was someone who looked exciting or someone who looked safe? Maybe it was someone you thought would dominate you or someone you thought you could dominate? Perhaps it was someone who looked just like your favourite parent or maybe was the opposite of your least favourite parent!'

The expectations in looking twice may give a clue to what is driving the relationship at a level that may be only half-conscious. For whatever else one may have said to each other and to oneself over the years, there are often other things, not always expressed, that one expected from the relationship. The majority of couples can look back on that, laugh about it, talk about it and say, 'Well, a lot of water has gone under the bridge since then and we have found out much more about ourselves.' Not all relationships achieve that. The reason I mention this is because it's important that these other reasons, often hidden expectations in relationship, should be expressed because the more hidden the expectation, the more unexpected and bitter may be the reaction when the expectation is not met. This is one of the things that I have to deal with most frequently in relationships and marriages that break down. Subsequently the person finds in somebody else that thing that they thought they were going to get from their marriage. That thing was never fully discussed or expressed. They were never really honest and therefore never worked through it.

In the story of Hannah and Elkanah, Hannah was a very unhappy wife. Hannah's expectations of the marriage were not being fulfilled, nor were Elkanah's. He expected his wife to be content with him: 'Do I not mean more to you than ten sons?' And the truth was that he did not. But at least here was a marriage where eventually they reached the position of communication, where Hannah was prepared to be honest about her expectations. They did talk, and things began to happen. Perhaps they needed a third party, the marriage guidance counsellor, to enable the communication to take place.

To go back to our exercise, I always hope people will go away and talk about it afterwards. Many women do not know what their husbands saw in them. Many women are able to say what they saw in their husbands but many husbands, while not feeling negative about their wives, are never able to be positive either. I think of a couple that have allowed me to use this illustration. They were not particularly good looking and both of them would have admitted that. The wife had very low self-esteem; her husband was a very kindly, safe character who was non-communicative – rather like Elkanah perhaps – and she never knew why he chose her. She knew why she chose him – he was so stable, rock-like and steady. One day as I was asking him this question in the consulting room he blushingly said, 'I saw an attractive pair of legs at a party and I looked up and she was on top of them!' She glowed and said, 'I always thought my legs were the nicest bit about me!' It had taken him 18 years to communicate the first compliment to his wife that she could accept as being valid.

This lack of talking, lack of confiding, of sharing in this way, erodes confidence in a marriage. It has been shown that 40% of women who do not feel a close, confiding relationship become depressed, whereas only 4% of women who say they have a confiding relationship in their marriage become depressed. The absence of that confiding relationship makes them more vulnerable to the other things that happen. Open, honest communication is very important.

The second point is generosity. Generosity means thinking of the other person; it's the opposite of 'me-ism'. One of the popular views of marriage is that it's a 50/50 contract and natural reactions are to withdraw if the other partner withdraws. If you don't give me that, I won't give you this – and so you get a 40/40 relationship, 30/30, and eventually nothing and then split. Both parties feel hurt, wounded, wary, resentful and very susceptible to other people who come along and who seem to be much more kind, thoughtful and someone to whom you can talk.

No. Marriage is a 100%/100% relationship, then when one fails totally there is still 100% left. When Hannah did not conceive, instead of reducing his commitment to her, which he could have done, and indeed in his culture he would have been expected to do, Elkanah doubled his commitment to her to show that he loved her. Although she bore him no son to perpetuate his name, to work in his fields, to bring honour to him in his society, nevertheless he gave her a double portion. He went out of his way to demonstrate affection and understanding, even when she was obviously miserable.

This principle of going the extra mile, of bringing forgiveness when we are wrong, extra when we are short-changed, is so imbedded in scripture and yet so difficult to maintain. It is one of the principles of Christianity and of Christ's teaching; and yet people find the principle a real stumbling block. When things go wrong in a relationship, instead of recrimination, retrenchment, no sex, no speak, the Christian principle is an acknowledgement of our own contribution to the row and a using of the situation to learn. When expectations are not met in a relationship – either partner not achieving in their job or losing their attractiveness – it calls for a new kind of love and support. We should add something new and extra to the relationship. Instead of looking at what one is not getting out of the relationship, the Christian way is an acknowledgement of what we are receiving from the relationship and looking at the ways in which we feel bigger, better, more complete because we are married to that person.

Sometimes, even when we try all that, we still seem to get it wrong and we catch it in the neck. We try to show our love as best we know how and even that is rejected as not love. I think of so many couples who say, 'I give her this, I give her that. I would not do that if I did not love her.' She says, 'But that is not what I mean.' So another little exercise that I sometimes do here is to say, 'Ask each other for something that the other person can do for you, just to show that they really love you; something that you would like and which that person can really fulfil – and it must be something that is positive; it must not be 'stop nagging' but something positive, something to do, not something to stop. It must be repeatable, so it's not just a one-off like giving a new car, and it must be kept up even if the other lapses during the week.' It is that practising of generosity, that thinking of the other person. This may be a behavioural technique but it is there in the New Testament: 'Whatever things are lovely, pure, of good report, think on those things.' I think of a couple (to whom I'm also very grateful for allowing me to give the example), both of them working, both of them high-powered, both totally immersed in their careers. They would both come in from work and she would feel cross with him because he was not showing her the kind of affection she wanted, and he would feel hurt because she was so cross, and they were beginning to drift apart. So I said, 'Well, what can you do for each other?' Eventually they managed to come round to this: that he would make the coffee after she had made the meal. He said, 'But I'm tired', and she said, 'What do you think I am? I'm working all day too and then I have to make the meal and then you expect me to make the coffee too?' 'Alright, I'll make the coffee'; and then what would she do for him? He said, 'If only she would just kiss me goodbye in the morning and say, 'Have a good day, dear'.' She said, 'I'm not that sloppy sort of person, you knew that!', and he looked a bit hurt so she said, 'Oh, well OK.'

I talked to them a month later and asked how things were going. They were beaming all over their faces and said they had not done too badly. She said, 'Great – I make the meal, I relax and he brings the coffee – it's superb. We actually then do the dishes together.' He beamed all over his face, quite proud of himself. And what about the other bit? 'Oh, well,' she said, 'that was going alright until we had a real blistering row one morning and I slammed out the room, went down the garden path, slammed the gate, into the car, slammed the door – and then got out, walked up the path, opened the door, went in, gave him a peck on the cheek and said, 'Damn, Dr Barker!'.' (Sorry for the verbatim!) But he knew how much that had cost her, he knew therefore that that was an act of generosity beyond what he had experienced before where that extra step occurred even when one partner was feeling wounded.

There is a dimension even beyond honesty and generosity, and that is what I call a 'mutual self-giving'. This is one of the most difficult things of all. Ephesians 5:21 speaks about marriage and relationships and it begins with the phrase, 'Submit to one another out of reverence for Christ', and then it goes on to talk about wives submitting to husbands, husbands loving their wives and the relationship between children and parents, workers and employers. But at the heart of this is the concept of submitting to one another, and 'submit' is a difficult word. When we use words like 'submit' or 'obey', we are using words that have been twisted away from their New Testament significance. We mean control, rather than something that you give to the other person. I like the word 'deferring' as it has that idea of voluntarily giving, putting ourselves that little bit lower than the other person out of love for that person. Our fulfilment in marriage can only be achieved by surrendering something of our doing-our-own-thing, our being ourselves, for the sake of the other person and out of love for that other person.

If there is Christian teaching for marriage, this is it. Here is the dimension that Christ brings into relationships, into marriage, into the relationship between parents and children, worker and employer, which is so different from anything else that I know of. We do it because Christ loved us in that way. We do it for each other because in some way it is that which causes a greater relationship in a marriage than just our fulfilling our own selves within marriage. The modern idea of 'my' fulfilment in marriage is self-centred. The biblical view is deferring to each other, an acting together, a preparedness to spend and be spent for each other: a mutual submissiveness to Christ and, because of that, to each other. Any submission that produces a sense of being crushed is not Christian, it's sub-Christian. A Christian submission should give a liberation, a new dimension, not enabling us to do our own thing better but enabling a new thing and new things to emerge from our joint relationship: one joined to one not making two, but a larger one.

Let me just take a very simple example. So often when we look at our home it is considered the husband's retreat – and if the wife has a job outside it is her retreat too. When there are young children, the home often becomes the prison of the wife and the retreat of the husband. In our mutual submission to each other the one who has the outside job should recognise the need of the other person to get out; and the one who has the inside job should recognise the need of the other to get back. It is in that tension of seemingly competitive needs that the home acquires a new dimension, a haven that is outward looking. How you work that out differs from one family to another according to their background and how they see things. However, it is something that must be tackled. When we look at hobbies, the hobbies of the one may isolate the other, the golf widow, for instance. But in our mutual submission something new should emerge.

In the New Testament the marriage relationship is an experience of surrender without domination, of service without compulsion, of love without conditions. Richard Holloway, a former Bishop of Edinburgh, said that in it are illustrated, as far as such divine realities can be illustrated by analogies with human experience, all the truths of God's love and grace. We shall look at this more when we come to look at bringing up our children and living with our teenagers in the following chapters.

Chapter Two
MAKING GOOD PARENTS

It has been said that there are two things one should never do: the first is to spend other people's money, and the second is to bring up other people's children! No one is an expert in child rearing or in parenting. Each child is different, and those who think they have it all mastered after child number seven need to think again, for the eighth may not be like any of the others. I do not have eight so I cannot speak from personal experience, but I can speak from the experience of dealing with parents of 8, 9, 10 and even 13 children! Even for those who think they have mastered child rearing, their experience will have changed in between each child. Parents are learning all the time; each child is different and parents behave differently with each child. Every family is an experiment in child rearing.

What if one comes from a split home? What if someone spent their own teen years in rebellion? What if a person experienced rejection or abuse as a child? How then does one react to bringing up one's own children? How often does one hear spouses saying to each other, 'You're just like your mother when you say that', or, 'You're just like your father when you do that'? In times of stress we tend to reach for the model we know best and then later are often appalled at how we have behaved. Not all people react in this way: some overreact and become the opposite of what their parents were like.

When one enters parenthood, whether by accident or design, it is important to look at the models, the anti-models, the expectations and the experiences that are brought to that situation. Some of those models may have been thought through, whereas others may not have been. Many parents do not have a partner or have lost a partner; others may have had one or two partners. Our past experiences are significant and often underestimated. Speaking personally, I am reminded that it was not until I was in my forties that I realised that for four years I was brought up in a one-parent family. My father was called up during the Second World War and spent those years in the Far East and suddenly I, as the eldest child of three, was the man about the house. I had to grow up, and lost four years of childhood.

As a psychiatrist with children I am somewhat nervous about talking about parenthood. Just as people get a perverse pleasure from seeing cobblers' children with holes in their shoes, so children of vicars and psychiatrists are often scrutinised by the curious, and some get a sense of satisfaction when they see problems occurring in these children. It happened to me at a conference when I was one of the speakers. My wife and family were asked to come as well. After my talk the person who ran this centre said, 'You cannot blame us for looking with curiosity at how your children are doing. After all, psychiatrists' children have a certain curiosity value: you'll be glad to know we gave you almost full marks!' I felt terribly threatened by that; the children were one and a half and three years old. I thought, 'How dare they judge my family life in that way!'

Princess Diana was a young mother from a broken home with enormously high expectations laid upon her and her children. Talking to a group of family specialists in this area she said, 'There are certain common ingredients essential for families of all sizes and types. There must be love, but love in its most practical form, commitment to each other, sharing together, self-discipline and some self-sacrifice. I doubt whether there is any standard formula for a successful family. The family is, after all, the most human and hence the most imperfect of institutions.... mothers, fathers and children who simply do their best with what they have...' A very powerful, poignant and telling quote.

What about some of the attitudes to parenting and the modern family? What has happened to families over the centuries? I want to concentrate particularly on the last hundred years. What is it that we see when we look at the modern family? First, there is an intensified bonding within the nuclear family. A nuclear family is mum, dad, or perhaps a surrogate parent, and the children. The bonding that takes place has intensified increasingly over the past 150 years. This is partly due to the mobility of our population, which takes the family away from grandparents, brothers, uncles and aunties and other close relations. It is partly due to the generational independence of older people who want to stay where they are, with all their friends, and not necessarily move to be near their family. Older people these days carry on working until 60 or 65 or even older and then they want to do things in their retirement and not necessarily take over looking after their grandchildren. When I first worked as a psychiatrist in the east of Scotland in the 1960s, it was the grandmothers who brought up the children while the mothers went out to work. Nowadays grandmothers want to carry on their jobs and holiday in the Costa Brava, and the mothers are told, 'You've had your children, you look after them!'

Second, there is the drive to individualism, 'my' needs; 'Why should I take over a role for other people's children? Oh, it's nice to have them but it's nice to get rid of them too!' I'm sure every grandparent says that. They like to see them but, oh what a relief when they go off! The jargon phrase that is used is that children are now 'enmeshed' with their parents. Interaction with their parents is concentrated and the more so when they are the only child or children of one-parent families. These children often have no peers to whom they can relate, and not infrequently only one parent. To pool affection one has to look for other ways in which these children can relate to peers or other parental authorities, otherwise in such families there is a claustrophobic relationship. That is not to say that all single children do worse than children in big families; often they do rather better since more time is spent with them. However, they do have to learn how to socialise, how to be angry and how to receive anger in different ways. All the research shows that single-parent families are disadvantaged. A single parent has less time to spend with their child, although they may have a much closer relationship with them and this intensified bonding may lead to enmeshment.

Third, the smaller family gives rise to special and wanted children of whom a lot is expected. There are not so many unplanned children now. Desperately wanted children often bring with them high expectations from the parents. I can think of parents who said, 'We had only one child because we wanted them to go to the best school and we could not afford it for more than one.' That was the motivation for the one child per couple in China. It was not just to bring down the population but also to raise the standard of living and bring the good things of life to those children who were born. Research suggests that these children receive enormous love and care, but face high expectations as well and it becomes a pressured relationship. The parents' reaction to their 'only' child is, 'We only have you, what are you going to produce, with all the things we have given you?'

The next thing that has happened in the modern family is the change in emphasis and the importance of the child's welfare, which has led to parental insecurity. Until about 1890, fathers had exclusive rights. Mothers did not have the same rights to their children until 1973. It was Doctor Barnardo, a Christian philanthropist in the nineteenth century, who in a landmark case challenged the exclusive right of one father to have a child returned to him so that he might sell the child to an Italian organ grinder. By the 1970s children could be removed by the State when the physical and emotional welfare of the child was threatened. In 1989 the Children's Act stated that in any family dispute what is right for the child is paramount. This has led to a certain insecurity in parenting.

The following excerpt, from a textbook on principles of family law, shows how things have changed. A judge in the 1920s said of a little girl who had lived with her foster parents for seven years and was due to go back to her natural parents, 'I can quite understand that this little girl will be greatly distressed and upset at parting from her foster parents, but at her tender age one knows from experience how mercifully transient are the effects of partings and other sorrows and how soon the novelty of fresh surroundings and new associations effaces the recollection of former days and kind friends, and I cannot attach much weight to this aspect of change.'

Since then the world has changed and with it people's attitudes. This leads me to my fourth point. Nowadays parents feel insecure and uncertain how to be good parents. This has given rise to the increased input of child psychology and the plethora of 'how-to' books. In the past, among the upper classes you had a nanny and the child was handed over to her. Nannies were trained. I remember a nanny once said to me: 'Nanny-children are always better brought up; they know not to pick their noses'! When people began to go up the social scale but couldn't afford nannies, they had to learn how to cope.

Some of the older generation were brought up by the Truby King method. I managed to rescue one such book from the rubbish heap in my parents' home: *Feeding & Care of Baby* (1922), a medical directory of babies of the Empire. Here is the advice she gave in her chapter entitled 'The 25 Errors in Child Upbringing': 'When a baby cries the natural and proper course is to give him the breast or bottle or a comforter to comfort or pacify him.... false or true? False. There is no surer way of ruining a baby's digestion and converting him into a fretful, exacting little tyrant who knows he can get his way by merely crying. Feed by the clock at duly appointed meal-times only. Comforters spoil digestion and give rise to defective teeth, deformed jaws and adenoids.'

The next generation followed Dr Spock, who advocated free expression. Parents feared to discipline at all and little tyrants were produced. Later came Dobson, the guru of the Christian family. Good old-fashioned values were back, parent power was in again: 'dare to discipline' and 'love must be tough'. Parents said, 'Oh boy, power is back in our hands again!' A Christian critique with which I totally agree is that this is culturally biased and not necessarily Christian. A very shrewd comment was made that Dobson dedicated his books to his father, whom he adored, but you hardly heard anything about his mother. Beware of books that say, 'Here is the real way to parenthood.'

The truth is that styles of parenting are very culture-bound and what is called 'Biblical parenting' in much of popular Christian literature is very much a response to current culture. It is really very little different from the Daily Telegraph, August 1988, 'The right way to bring up children', which included some very odd phrases. The heading is 'Thatcherite academics call for a return to traditional methods in the post-permissive age'. I would say beware. We may be seeking old-fashioned values that really have lost their place. We may be refusing to understand the good reasons why changes have come about: that mothers do have rights, that children do have welfare to be considered and that children are developing persons. Grandparents are living longer and independently and are not around – rightly perhaps.

The Bible gives very few prescriptions for parenting. It just describes family life as it is with some rather hair-raising examples of parenthood. King David is one of the more instructive stories. He was too busy to know what his sons were up to. He was busy travelling up and down the country, conquering people, often away from home, absorbed in his work and yes, he was good at his job, but he was out of touch with his sons. He had never got around to sorting out the difficulties at home and when one son abused his sister, another older son found out, was furious and chased the younger brother off. David knew what was going on and was very cross but did nothing. The older son was aware of this and waited for his opportunity, which occurred when the sons were going on an outing. The father should have gone with them but was too busy to go. The sons went out on their own and the older brother took the opportunity to kill the offending younger brother. In the event Absalom, the older brother, lost all respect for his father, revolted against him and eventually was killed, leading to that heart-rending cry of David: 'Absalom, my son, Absalom, oh my son: would that I had died instead of you!'

A dramatic story, but it does draw attention to one aspect of parenting, for good parenting means spending time with the children. One has no option when a child is small, one has to spend time with them constantly and just to have a little bit of respite is tremendous. The need to give time remains part of good parenting right up until adulthood, but in different ways as they get older. Historically mothers have had to do most of the early caring and fathers did not do very much.

Fathers should make themselves available to their growing children. How many biographies portray Dad as a stranger? The child is often uncertain as to what father is really like or what he feels or thinks. John Newton, the great hymn-writer, said, 'I knew my father loved me but he was unable to show it.' Many fathers are never even around to show it. Fathers often overinvest in their work and leave the responsibility of their young child to their wives. They take little time off to keep their marriages in good shape and do too little to further their relationship with their children.

There is a problem for the wives who are surrounded by four-year-old conversation all day. The husband comes in tired and of course does not want to say too much but just flops in front of the television. Fathers, and increasingly mothers too, have invested a great deal of time in providing a good standard of living and ensuring a good education for their children. That is not the same as educating and training them for life. I have had fathers who say that they are glad of the extra duties and on-call work that keeps them at the office, clinic or hospital until the children are in bed!

The children need time and involvement. I know some would say, 'Ah, but we spend quality time.' I will never forget the Reverend Paul Berg, vicar of our church in Bristol, preaching one evening on quality time: 'Good, we have an hour of quality time, let's do something. What are we going to do…? Pack your bags, in the car and let's go out …' You feel absolutely exhausted before you have even got into your quality time because everything has to be extracted out of this short time. The kind of time I mean is not that kind of quality time. The time I mean is recognised as their time, not our guilt time that we spend with the children, but time that is the child's, that is secure, bespoken, sacrosanct, predictable. There must be a time when families can share, tease, question and argue.

In preparing this I have consulted with my children. I learnt very early on not to stand in a pulpit and refer to my children or even make allusions to parenting, without checking with them beforehand. We were reminiscing about them as children and us as parents. They said, 'Our Saturdays were tremendous. We had special treats that we remember. We knew you were going to be around and even if it was only to play with our toys, we knew you were there.' They went on to say that Sunday mornings were also special: we were together. There were treats such as croissants, we were relaxed, we talked, we were on our own. We did not have visitors and we knew that that was when we got the feedback on what was going on. The things that we had forgotten to discuss with them, the things that we had involved ourselves in that had implications for them and that they had thoughts about, but we had not thought they would actually even notice. That extra half-hour before Family Service was well used. The children were awake and up, it was only we who had to make the sacrifice and get up. When they were older there were fewer predictable times, but this regular demand for availability was still essential.

Parenting means encouraging and this is a special word and work for fathers. There is only one injunction to parents that I know of in the New Testament and it is, 'Dads, do not irritate your sons' – and that includes daughters! Until recently it was universally assumed that children were to obey their parents and fathers had total rights. Obedience is fine but when you give fathers total rights, you get something rather nasty. In the ancient world unwanted children were exposed and allowed to die. These tyrannical norms were unquestioned. Parents had total rights over their children and children had to obey. In contrast, Paul in his letter to the Ephesian Christians, in chapter six, says, 'Fathers, don't over-correct and make it difficult for your children to obey.' In the letter to the Colossians 3:20,21, JB Phillips translates, 'Otherwise they will grow up feeling inferior and frustrated'. Paul is quite clear: there is a reciprocal obligation. The obedience of the child is met with the encouragement and the reasonable discipline of the parent.

There is a Jewish saying: 'Fathers are always trying to make their sons into good Jews. When will they try to be good Jews instead of leaving the task to their sons?' I think that could also be said for some Christians. So much traditional Christian teaching is about children honouring and obeying their parents' instructions and of not sparing the rod. In the New Testament emphasis is on encouragement. The dominant New Testament theme within family life is the mutual obligation of child to parent and of parent to child. We do not demand our rights; we ensure the rights of others in the family relationship. In the previous chapter on marriage I quoted from Ephesians 5:21, which can be translated as 'Defer to one another.' We show that respect, which goes out of its way to ensure the rights of the other. That begins early on and increasingly must be something to which we pay attention. One cannot learn that too early.

On one occasion on holiday, we had gone to a restaurant wearing our best bibs and tuckers. Our six-year-old son was wearing a brand-new jacket that he had been given for a recent wedding. He looked at the menu and decided what to have. I said to the waitress, 'We will have so-and-so...and the little boy will have...', at which he interrupted, 'Dad, I'm not a little boy!' He was quite right. I had diminished him in public. 'I am a young man!' which he was, he had on his special jacket and was dining out with his parents.

Discipline should be on grounds that are clear, consistent and intelligible. King David's family was in chaos because they had no boundaries. He had committed adultery and murder and had real hang-ups in areas with which he had never come to terms or dealt with, and this in turn led to problems with discipline in his family. Both parents and children need control, limits and education.

Discipline of small children in my view should be related immediately to the situation and never saved up in the 'You wait until your father comes in' way. I don't know how other people deal with this but somehow one has to find a way in which it is dealt with as quickly as possible and not saved up, and it must be consistent and not erratic. What the generation of today does may be different to past or future generations.

With our children we had a little ploy where we had a cooling-off period. My wife used to say, 'I'll count to three! One, two...', and they would go off and do what we had asked them to do. Sometimes the 'one, two' begins to get a bit longer. Once you start finding that you have had 'one, two, two-and-a-half, two-and-three-quarters', you know you've lost! Our children knew what was happening but they knew there was a limit and the limit was the cloakroom. 'Do you want to visit the cloakroom?' The cloakroom was where private rebuke was administered. We did not do it in public, and if we got to the cloakroom then it did happen and that gave a funny type of security. It cleared the air. On one occasion we talked about the law in Sweden that said parents should not punish their children. Our children initially thought, 'What a fantastic law!' Then they said, '...but what are all the nasty things you would do instead! We'd rather have it dealt with there and then and forgotten.'

As children grow, other sanctions have to be used. The boundaries and limits must be expanded and they must be encouraged to explore those. I remember one child psychiatrist using an analogy that I like. He said, 'The whole question of discipline is rather like being in a boxing ring and you are increasing the size of the ring, you are extending the ropes, giving them a larger and larger area to spar in and to find where the ropes are.'

Third, parenting means providing a place of security and belonging. Children need a base to launch off from. The Psalmist says God's love is so great that he 'sets the lonely in families', Psalm 68:6. The danger is that within the family we may look upon the children as belonging to us in such a way that they have to fight to get free. Instead of children feeling a sense of belonging within the family, they sometimes get the feeling that they belong to the parents, that they are owned by the parents. They may feel they are needed by the parents, that their parents are investing in them and in their education. But children are not our goods. I remember being appalled at one of my relatives saying about his new son, 'Look what I have created – what we have made!' We provide physical and emotional security. We provide the knowledge of being loved. We encourage their gifts and their skills but we do not own them. They may bring us much happiness in return but we can never demand it. There is a constant theme in scripture of giving of children back to God. Remember Hannah's longing for a child, but she handed that child Samuel back to God. Families should be places of security and belonging that provide a place to explore the world. Our children do not belong to us, however much we may need them.

Finally, parenting involves providing goals. A family is a place where children gain their frame of reference, and acquire meaning, purpose, morals and identity. The family gives a frame of reference that enables the child ultimately to make decisions. One gives instructions, guidelines and examples. Children do not tolerate ambiguity, they need clarity and consistency. They need to know what we think and why we think as we do and act as we do. They need to know what we think about each other, about life, about them, about God. Parents do have to make decisions for their children but the basis of their decisions must be open to scrutiny and questioning.

Family life is a learning experience and our children should be helping us clarify our own goals. They should be asking us questions that cause us to say, 'Whoops, I hadn't thought of that!', and enable us to grow as people as well as parents. But so often the child looks at the parents' values and behaviour, and looks at what is done and what is not done, and asks, 'Why, what difference will it make?' Very often the answer comes back, 'Because it's the done thing' or 'Because it's not done', and there's an unresolved question. There's something unclear and inconsistent in that.

All of us fall far short in all sorts of ways. We have not measured up as well as John & Daisy or Mike & Mary; they seem to have got it right, don't they? I can only say to you that those apparently successful Johns & Daisies, Mikes & Marys, have areas of pain: areas where they do not dare let other people know what is going on. I see many couples who are apparently successful, with successful family lives. However, when you are taking a life history you may see them in the anguish and the pain of another issue in their lives. There may be very painful areas that nobody else knows about. None of us are perfect parents. None of us will have perfect children. Perfection is not this side of eternity and as Samuel Rutherford, the great Scottish theologian, said: 'If contentment were here, heaven would not be heaven.'

Chapter Three
ENJOYING THE TEEN YEARS

When my daughter heard that I was speaking on this subject she wrote and said, 'Do send me a copy please. It will be interesting to know how it feels in retrospect!' I can tell you now that the early years were years of excitement, seeing the children grow and their personalities develop, although sometimes it was a slog – just the sheer hard work of having two young children close together. The teen years were like being on a roller-coaster. There were times when one said, 'Hold tight!' as one went down. Then up you would go and enjoy the marvellous vistas and joy of being 'on the up'.

I want to focus upon the enjoying, but I will not miss out the downs. I would like to say right at the start that there is no formula on offer. One teenager behaves quite differently from another, even in the same family with the same parents and the same upbringing. Parents themselves also react differently. In our family there is a piece of wisdom going back at least a hundred years, which says, 'Teenage boys should be buried at 14 and not dug up again until they are 21!' On the other hand, we had a friend who once said to us, before we had teenagers, 'It is such fun having a teenage daughter!' I doubt if it is a matter of the difference between boys and girls, though they are different. It is more likely a difference in the particular teenager and perhaps even the difference in a particular parent's expectations and handling of the teenager. There is no evidence that a smooth adolescence bodes ill for the future, so do not be too alarmed if you are having a fairly easy run – next time may be very different.

Research indicates that 85% of teenagers like their parents, respect them and get on with them – at least that is what they told the researcher! A London child psychiatrist, Professor Michael Rutter, said: 'Adolescents turn to their parents for guidance on major interests and concerns. They turn to their peers for general interest in fashion and in leisure. Many of the altercations are minor, regarding such areas as clothes, hairstyles and tidiness.'

Family life is hard work. All relationships need effort and patience and if we enter any aspect of family life with negative attitudes then we will have negative reactions. However, if we enter with an expectation of enjoyment, at least we will be on the lookout for those more positive times. I do not intend to go into the psychological issues; this is not a treatise on adolescence as such. That is available in a number of books, including *Understanding Adolescence* by Roger Hurding.

There are several examples of teenagers in the Old Testament. Jacob was a cheat and a mummy's boy; Joseph was a creep and a daddy's boy; Absalom, David's son, felt he was nobody's boy and was rebellious. In the New Testament there is only one example of a lad growing up and that is Jesus himself. In chapter two of Luke's Gospel we see Jesus growing up from the baby in verse 12 to the little boy in verse 40 and to the lad in verse 43. The part of that account in Luke 2 appropriate to our subject is of the boy Jesus in the Temple. In his thirteenth year, Jesus was about to become Bar Mitzvah, a son of the Temple, a son of the Law, a boy who from that time on would be responsible for his actions to God and man. His parents had gone off to a special jamboree in Jerusalem and at the end of the visit they were dismayed when they had gone a day's journey and found that Jesus was not among the group. They had to trek back to Jerusalem and there they found him in the Temple, asking questions of the Rabbis with those in the Temple asking, 'Who's this lad? What clever questions he asks!'

Joseph and Mary were taken aback, astonished at their Jesus. They did not know that he had such talent. However, it was not long before parental authority asserted itself and Mary said,

'What a way to treat us! Your father and I were sick with worry searching for you.' Jesus needed to remind them why he was in the Temple, that he had actually been taking this visit to Jerusalem and to the Temple seriously. He was just about to become a son of the Temple, a son of the Law. Where else did they expect to find him but talking with the teachers, the Rabbis, discussing and asking questions like a good adolescent? We read that Mary thought about these things, pondering them in her heart.

Years ago we had a family discussion on the subject of parents, teenagers and teenage rebellion. One of our teenagers said, 'Dad, teenagers were not invented in your day, and in any case, you would not recognise teenage rebellion if you saw it! We have been such model teenagers!' The other one was a bit more reflective and what follows comes from that reflection on parents and teenagers. The first thing that was said was, 'Teenagers need to assert that they are grown up.' The teenager is aware of being grown-up but not quite sure how to handle it. They must explore new territory, must try things out and learn how to separate from their parents. If the parent is too protective or heavy handed then the teenager is not sure if they can be independent. Therefore they feel they must assert themselves and might even have to rebel, just to be sure that they can be grown up and independent.

If a parent has everything planned out for the teenager – which school and university they are going to attend, the profession they are going to follow, the business they are going to take over, the interests they are going to pursue – such parents may be in for a surprise! The teenager may have inherited our nose and perhaps learned our mannerisms but they do not necessarily acquire our interests and ways of reacting. We should be prepared to be surprised by our children and be open to the unexpected. We should try to anticipate their growing up and forging ahead of us in areas that we have no experience of at all. Joseph and Mary clearly had misjudged the situation with Jesus. They were obviously still treating him as a lad, apparently unaware of his growing consciousness of his special calling and destiny.

Teenagers today have special problems. Physically they are mature at a much earlier age than they were 20, 40, 60 or 100 years ago, so the period of adjustment to adulthood has been lengthened. In our society old age has been postponed due to such factors as nutrition, good health and medical care. These days one is only old really by the time one is in ones eighties or even nineties. When I am in India speaking to students and I ask, 'How old are your parents?' they say, 'Oh, very old.' 'How old?' I ask. 'Oh, late fifties!' comes the reply. The expectation of life in India is 56. So, we have postponed old age, but we have also shortened childhood. Childhood stops earlier, puberty is at least five years earlier than it was a hundred years ago. Children are much taller, but even if we have shortened childhood, we do not allow them into adulthood until they are 18! We keep them at school longer, so there is a much longer in-between time, and it is that which has been to some extent exploited, with a teenage culture that is seeking a peer identity. They have more money, and more physical and sexual maturity than before. Therefore they need to assert their being grown-up.

Second, the teenager needs limits and boundaries. Teenagers need a baseline from which to venture forth; they need a position that they can challenge and against which they can flex their muscles. I was recently in church and as we were singing one of the hymns noticed two children having a bit of a barney, and their parents then had to exert a little discipline, one of them moving in between them to separate them. That set the boundary and solved that problem.

Teenage years have been said to be a return of the toddler years and the parent who has never set limits for the toddler will have greater difficulties in setting limits later. Our teenager said, 'We must be allowed to feel grown-up but we must not have full control because we are not quite ready.' I was staggered! The teenager went on to say, 'We need to know what you think but you will have to make it convincing! We need something to push against but we need to know when we've reached the limit.' In Skinner and Cleese's book, *Families and How to Survive Them,* they say, 'Hell hath no fury like a teenage girl who has not been forced to help with the washing-up!' Teenagers want house rules. They may learn independence by not always doing what the parents want but we can enjoy the experience of being challenged, of being forced to think, of having our horizons broadened and being educated. We should be prepared to be teased, though we may have to set limits on what we are prepared to accept in terms of rudeness. We should be open to being challenged and not always determined to win the argument, which I have to admit I like to do, to the occasional demoralisation of my family. We should be able to accept the rejection of our views, but making it clear where we stand and why we stand there on such issues as sex, drugs, drinking and others that will come up and need discussion.

Do we know why we set the limits where we do? Do we know why we adopt the attitude we do? Do our teenagers see examples and models in our lives for the things that we say? 'Don't do what I do, do what I say' used to be the line, but that will not do today. King David was an absent father who left a moral vacuum, so his family life was seething in discontent and rebellion. We have to set the limits, we have to say why and be prepared to discuss why. We may have to modify our views as we learn another way of looking at things. We must be prepared to relinquish control gradually, broadening the distance between the ropes in the boxing ring.

It is of interest that following the interchange in the Temple between Jesus and his mother, Luke notes, 'Jesus went down to Nazareth with his parents and was obedient to them.' Remember that Luke must have either been quoting Jesus' own account of those events or, probably more likely, Mary's account, as she later discussed her experiences in bringing up Jesus.

We should beware of imposing sanctions that cannot be enforced. There are sanctions that one will be able to impose at 12, but not at 14, 16 or 17. One must also be prepared for the ultimate sanction, which is leaving the teenager to feel the consequences of their own decisions and actions.

The third point that was made was, 'When things go wrong, keep cool.' I was not sure I agreed with that one, but the more I think about it, the more I am sure that was right. I had to learn that blazing rows produce blazing reactions. That does not mean one should not show anger. Speaking personally, I had what used to be called 'Dad's moments'. That meant that my eyes popped, my finger wagged, my voice went up and I used to see them eventually giggling and saying, 'Oh, Dad's having one of his moments.' I made the point, but they also took the point and it became good-natured. One could laugh, and they could say of that aspect of my behaviour, 'No, that won't quite do!' Our children learn from our behaviour. The examples that we give, so often are the examples that are copied. Battering parents were often themselves battered children.

Some Christian parents go in for deep heart to heart sessions and one should beware of this. So often such sessions put emotional pressure on what is still an unequal relationship. On some occasions straight things do need to be said to clear the air, but parents need to be aware of secondary agendas. Edmund Gosse was a celebrated literary figure of the late nineteenth century. He wrote a sad autobiography called *Father and Son*, in which he described the relationship between his father and himself. He was brought up in a Christian home and his father was a famous scientist. Gosse craved his father's friendship but his father never allowed himself to be a friend to his son. On the other hand, the father longed that his son should share his Christian faith, which did not happen. So, the son craved friendship and the father pleaded for his son's salvation, and they never met. Jesus' mother, Mary, did not understand what was happening to her son. More than once she indulged in remonstrating with him. But she pondered these issues. No doubt she prayed over these issues, until one day she understood what it meant.

It is important for parents to get their motivation, their goals and their aspirations clear in their own minds and to be careful where they set the boundaries to ensure that they are not manipulating their children. Sometimes there is another agenda:

'What will people think? How can I keep my head up? We never thought this would happen in our family.' It is then that grandparents or the favourite uncle or aunt can have a special role to play. Then the teenagers know that they belong, that they are loved, but it removes that personal possession element in the relationship that may be present with the parents.

One of the special people in our family was an aunt who died in her late nineties. When she found she could not have children, her strong Irish mother told her, 'Look, there is plenty of work for a childless aunt in a large family such as ours; so get on with it!' At the time she was very upset. However, she was the one who related to all her nephews and nieces in a special way, so that visits to her home and Christmas presents from her were looked forward to with much greater anticipation than all the other aunts and uncles.

Occasionally the relationship can break down completely. There is an excellent book by John White entitled *Parents in Pain*. White was a student Christian leader in Manchester with a tremendous drive and vision. He became a medical missionary in South America and then worked as a psychiatrist in Canada. He was the author of several splendid books: *The Fight, The Cost of Commitment, People of Prayer*. He was a celebrated Bible teacher, both in North America and the UK. In his very last paragraph of *Parents in Pain* he says, 'Why do you think I wrote this book? I have not written as a psychiatrist to readers who might benefit from my professional knowledge but as a parent who has tasted the bitterness of despair and found a larger God as a result of groping in the darkness. The book is an invitation to join the fellowship of parents in pain – or rather, of parents who through pain have grasped the hand of a larger, more powerful and more tender God than we ever knew existed.' There is not much enjoyment, but there is a far, far deeper experience of human life, of parenting and of God, which undoubtedly came out in White's later books.

Sometimes, a 'parentectomy' is essential. Just as one has an appendicectomy because of pain in the belly, on occasions it is necessary to separate the teenager from the parent. Ideally, there is a relationship between the parents and the adolescent that enables that adolescent to come and go with greater and greater ease, keep in contact, wave goodbye and bounce back from time to time. Sometimes there is something awry within that relationship. Either the teenager is too clinging to one or other parent or the parent, for one reason or another, is too bonded to the teenager. That can be a painful situation. There may be smiles on the surface but tears inside. Sometimes there are tears on the outside too. In certain medical conditions (anorexia, depression in adolescence and various other issues) something has to be done to break the bonding and enable the teenager to leave. This can be very difficult. The teenager realises they have to make the break and in seething anger, off they go without looking back. Parents feel they have failed but it may not be their failure. It may be something within that teenager that they can only express and deal with in that way. However, as Christian parents one can never say, 'That's the end.' We ourselves wandered off; we ourselves have often been in rebellion; we ourselves have received forgiveness and we must be prepared to accept our child back and grant forgiveness.

As Christians, we are not simply left to do the best with what we have. We are members of the family of God. Whatever our backgrounds, experiences or limitations, we and our families are part of that wider family. In church we often began our worship with the words: 'We have come together as the family of God in our, Father's presence, to ask his forgiveness, that we may give ourselves to His service' and that includes our service of bringing up children. In the church family we have other models of parenting and caring that we and our children can draw on. We belong to each other and we should draw from, care for and encourage each other. We ought to learn from each other, not only from other parents but also from singles, widows, the childless and the younger and older members of the fellowship.

Our family gained a great deal from the students we had babysitting for us in the early years. Later we had a student living in our top flat. These people became members of our extended family and they gave alternative peer models to our growing children. They came to have very special roles within the family, people our children could check-out with when Dad was being a bit difficult. Do not forget, in New Testament times many of the new Christians were people from very difficult backgrounds indeed: people from multiple divorces who had experienced physical violence, who had been sexually promiscuous. Within the fellowship and family of God they learnt new family relationships.

Some of us may feel very inadequate and we all do at times. We may feel that we have never fulfilled our parents' expectations of us and we may pass that on to our children, so that they never feel they fulfilled our expectations of them. But in God's family we do not hide away in shame: we come out and share. Some churches have coffee-time after the service. Is it just a social nicety? Do you discuss what you've learnt or do you just swap the achievements of your children? Do we use Sunday lunches as a time to introduce other people to our families? House Groups too can give so much. Our House Group has been one of the most supportive bodies in caring for us physically and emotionally. We need to learn how to share, how to support each other. It's very difficult when we are all expected to be 'copers'. Our teenagers know the areas where we do not cope as well. I think of people in our fellowship who contributed to our teenagers and to us. I think particularly of one elderly lady; she was old in years but tremendously young in spirit, without any family of her own, elderly, single. This woman had a very significant role when we had times of family crisis. Our young people loved her and had a tremendous respect and regard and affection for her. I think, too, of how I have sometimes given that sort of service to other people's teenagers. I remember once discussing an issue with a teenager. I said, 'You could have discussed that with your father, why didn't you?', and her comment was, 'I know what he would have said: I needed to check out elsewhere!' I'm glad I was able to give that service back, for I had years before received help from her father. We tried to have young couples in our home so that hopefully our kids could check their attitudes. You need these people who will bridge the gaps and the difficulties.

As Christians, we are members of a new family and we have experienced new beginnings and a new experience of forgiveness. We have experienced in Christ someone who made the first move in forgiveness to us. This is at the heart of all family relationships and it is unique to the Christian faith. Forgiveness of others is not essential in any other religion. You can do it if you want but it is not obligatory; but forgiveness is at the heart of the Christian Gospel and Christian life. Families are notorious for rifts and family gatherings are often fraught occasions when every Christmas may bring its rash of more family hurts. I have come across families who have cut off their sons and daughters. I have had to deal with some who have said, 'My son is dead, he no longer exists. His name is not to be mentioned.' In the Christian family there may be separation but there can never be rejection. Forgiveness is the removal of the barrier to reconciliation. It is the admission of things wrong and the remission of wrongs done. We believe it is possible for there to be forgiveness between two people and a new start, as though things had not happened. Christians know that is what has happened to them through Jesus Christ.

Paul Tournier, the Swiss physician, said, 'Forgiveness looks straight at the wrong, sees it in all its wrongness and then forgives because it is evil, just as God loves us because and in spite of our sins.' If we are loved like that, how can we refuse to show some inkling of that in our family relationships, especially when we ourselves are not without guilt. It is that dynamic of forgiveness that enables us not only to survive families but also to add a new dimension and remake family life.

Finally, we have in God, the Father, the Son and the Holy Spirit, the three persons of the Trinity. Within that there is a model from which all family-ness is derived. In Ephesians Paul, having talked about the family of God, continues in chapter 3:15: 'For this reason I kneel before the Father, from whom His whole family in heaven and on earth derives its name' (another translation is, 'from whom family-ness, father and mother together, derives its being'). What is the source of parenthood? It is God the Father. Forget the stereotypes that we have of fathering, this phrase means fathering and mothering together, both come from God the Father. Family-ness, what it is to be a family in the belonging and the relating, the independence and yet the oneness, is derived from the Trinity. This is what we mean when we talk about a personal God, from whom we are derived, from whom our family-ness is derived, from whom our mothering and our fathering is derived. We do not relate to our experience and say, 'That's what God is like', but we look at God the Father and say, 'That's where parenting comes from.'

The story of the Prodigal Son has been called the story of the Waiting Father; a teenage son had gone off but knew somewhere in the depths of his heart that it was possible to go back. Hosea, a man with a terrible family life, whose very name means 'faithful love', speaks of God having love that pursues and stays beside us even in the middle of rebellion. Hosea speaks of God saying, 'When Israel was a child I loved him. It was I who taught him to walk, it was I who bent down to feed him, it was I who carried his school bag, it was I who lifted him up in my arms.' That is mothering and there it is in Hosea 11. Hosea goes on, 'When Israel wandered off ... how can I give him up and hand him over? I'm not a man, I am God!' However discouraged we may be, however much we may feel there are no solutions to whatever is going on in our families – and I am talking here of the whole gamut of family relations – there may be resolution, even though there is no solution. We may not solve all the problems but with God's help we will maintain and improve the relationships.

I will never forget a patient of mine, a woman in her fifties, who came to see me over several weeks. I was going through her family relationships and she talked of how mother and father battled it out. It was difficult but somehow or other they stuck together. Then she stopped, almost as if something had suddenly struck her. A smile came over her face, a smile that I shall never forget, it was beautiful – and she said, not to me or to anyone, but to herself, 'But they stuck at it somehow, and now they seem to have got through all that. They're like Darby and Joan.' She had suddenly recognised in the middle of all the awfulness of family life (as to some extent she saw it when she was recounting it to me) something positive, something rich, something wholesome. Here was an example, a model of something that was good that she could draw from, which had become part of her life. I don't think she had seen it until that moment.

There are those within our fellowships who struggle against tremendous odds and continue to struggle. It reminds me of the story of Ruth, who had a hard life. She was widowed early in her marriage and her mother-in-law was likewise widowed, but Ruth remained with her mother-in-law. She eventually married Boaz, who was probably a very much older man, which most likely meant she was left a widow again eventually. It is a story of ordinary people, struggling with life, but God working through the committed relationships within that family. The story got into one of the Holy Books of Israel, so it is in our scriptures. I am reminded that out of that family, with all its problems and difficulties, came the Messiah, Jesus, Emmanuel, God with us. We do not know what the outcome of our family life, with all its difficulties, will be. We may be left with questions. We may sometimes feel our teenagers are not very enjoyable, but within the family of God, where we know God is our Father, the origin of all our family, there is a grace, there is a resolution that God will bring in His time.

ISSUES OF HEALTH

Chapter Four
SLEEPLESSNESS

When I was a house physician living in hospital on call, it was unusual to have an unbroken night, and on one of those rare occasions when I had managed to get to bed by midnight I was wakened at 1 o'clock in the morning by a roar from the room next door. The following morning I asked the colleague who occupied that room what the commotion had been and he said, 'It was night sister again. She rang me up and said, 'Dr Grubb, could I have some night sedation for Mrs Smith?' I asked her, 'Why? Is she is pain?', and Sister said, 'No, but she can't get to sleep'.' To which Dr Grubb replied, 'Nor can I', and slammed the phone down.

The sister's concern was perhaps less for her patient than for having a quiet night duty, but God is not as callous as that particular doctor was, to leave us to stew in our sleeplessness, rather he inspired his servant King David to compose an evening prayer for insomniacs.

The opening verses of Psalm 4 echo the cry of the sleepless person who is having a bad night after a bad day and is feeling trapped and hemmed in. The Psalmist asks the question: 'Why are you upset, why are you uptight? Part of your difficulty may be that you cannot make up your mind about God, you're so easily swayed by other people.' And don't we all recall a time when we have been tempted to question our commitment to God? We try to follow him and what happens? We get ridiculed, people misinterpret what we say; they tell lies about us, or they may mock us as the God Squad, the God botherers, Holy Joes, even hypocrites. If we are young, they say, 'Oh, you'll grow out of it, you know.' If we're old: 'Of course some people need a prop in life.' Not infrequently I have had it hinted to me that I follow a wrong god. I remember when I was a student, one of my fellow medical students shut his Bible very firmly and said, 'That book is beginning to get between me and what I really want to do in life. I'm going to shut it and not open it again'; and as far as I know he never did.

But the Psalmist says, 'Know that the Lord has set apart the godly, those who would follow him for himself.' God does not offer us ease, success, comfort, fame, praise – he offers himself, and only himself with no ifs and no bargains. We either follow him or we don't. We either are a member of his family or we are not. And we share the family fortunes with him.

We can express our doubts to God, but we dare not dither and swither in our commitment. Many people claim to be Christians but seem to make so little progress. Why? Is it because they live permanently provisional lives? They are not sure whether they want to follow God the whole way or maybe hang on to a few other gods just in case. And David says that this is a recipe for sleepless nights, as we dither about where we are going and whom we are following. Remember how Jesus said to his disciples in the Sermon on the Mount, 'No man can serve two masters.' Your mind should be set upon God's kingdom before anything else. 'Let tomorrow look after tomorrow, and today's troubles be kept to this day.' (Matt. 6:24,34)

Most of us will have had the experience at one time or another of lying in bed, wishing that sleep would come, but instead our mind is going over and over the events of the day, then perhaps events from other days are dragged up, and all sorts of bogeymen that we thought had disappeared begin to haunt us. It may be not so common when one is young, unless of course there is an exam coming the next morning that one has not prepared for, but when one gets older responsibilities begin to multiply, and sometimes sleep comes a little harder.

But insomnia tells us something. It's like pain – sometimes if we had no pain, we wouldn't know things were wrong – and when we have insomnia and are unable to sleep, it may point to some physical illness, it may indicate that we have some mental illness, but it can also be pointing to a personal or perhaps spiritual conflict in our lives.

In Psalm 4 the psalmist says that one of the things that can gnaw away at our brain and cause us to have sleepless nights is seething anger and resentment. The psalmist says, 'Yes, be angry but do not sin.' This is a phrase quoted by St Paul in his letter to the Ephesians 4:26 when he says, 'Be angry but do not sin. Don't let the sun go down while you are still angry.' It is so easy to get worked up if someone has hurt us, and even if we don't mean to, because we are so sensitive, that is the way we take it. We lie awake and we think, 'Why didn't I do such and such? Why didn't I think of that to say? Just wait till the next time he tries that.' And we get ourselves really worked up. I remember a colleague once said to me before a committee meeting, 'If someone gets one over you, just wait, because he is bound to make a mistake sometime and then there is your chance to pounce and say, 'Gotcha', and take him to the cleaners.' I wonder how many sleepless nights he spent hatching ways to do just that.

There is a place for anger: against injustice, against exploitation, against poverty, against blasphemy of God's name. But the psalmist says to us, 'When you are in your bed, search your own heart, be silent.' What the psalmist is encouraging us to do is to ask ourselves certain questions if we find ourselves in such a frame of mind. Have we never hurt others? Is the resentment that we are feeling and feeding really vengefulness? One of the advantages of lying on our own awake at night is that in the quietness it's just possible that God can get through to us and speak to us. In Deuteronomy 32:35, God says 'Vengeance in mine', and Paul in his letter to the Romans 12:19 quoting from this says 'Don't repay evil with evil but with good.'

It's often said that we should sleep on something before acting, but both the psalmist and St Paul say that we should do something before sleeping and that is repent. Resolve how we could act differently from the way in which the person has acted towards us – not in retaliation but in an attempt to restore. Some of us will call to mind the account of Gordon Wilson whose daughter was killed by the IRA and who said, 'I forgive those men', and sought to bring healing into that riven community. Our Lord gives us the same example. When we find ourselves seething with anger and are kept awake thinking resentful thoughts, we may well feel anger where it is just, but then we should go on to meditate on where we have hurt others, and look for what we can do that is healing and restoring.

Psalm 4 is not one of those spontaneous psalms that David composed when he felt really hard done by or on the contrary, when he felt absolutely thrilled by the goodness of God. It is a Psalm that seems to have been specially composed for Evening Prayer in the Temple. It was written with instructions for the choirmaster, and even the choice of instruments was laid down. No drums and cymbals, that would be far too stimulating at night, just strings, pleasant, quiet and meditative.

And so the psalmist addresses himself to all those who have lain awake at night overcome by feelings of despair, to those who say 'What's the good? Nothing pleasant ever happens to me. Why doesn't God smile on me?' And the psalmist says, 'Why do you keep asking God for a special blessing? Why do you keep asking for tokens of his power and of his love, as if he hasn't given you more than enough already?'

Just as there are some people who are never happy in a relationship unless they are getting constant affirmation, or feel that something's wrong if they're not getting lots of hugs or phone calls, so some Christians always long for reassurance and are never content, and are quickly discouraged if they do not get success in what they think they should be doing, or if they meet with disappointment. The psalmist is saying that the person who is truly committed and faithful to the Lord has a heart filled with greater joy than the happiness of a double harvest. Prosperity, goods and success can bring happiness – I'm happy when things like that happen to me – but a life linked to God brings joy and peace even in adversity and apparent failure.

People sometimes count sheep in order to get to sleep, but the psalmist is telling us that joy comes from counting our blessings. 'Lord, you have given me more joy in my heart than others ever know for all their corn and wine', as the Jerusalem Bible translates verse 7. Joy and peace are linked with contentment in both the Old Testament and the New. Christians are not told that they will be happy. Christians are told to rejoice: to rejoice at being in Christ's service, to rejoice at knowing that God will provide what we need and in so doing will equip us for our true place in his world. When Paul was writing to the Philippian church he said he had learnt the secret of facing plenty and hunger, abundance and want. He had learnt that secret, he explains, by rejoicing, by recalling all the things that others crave for, which after all are only the gifts of God's creation. Whereas others may exploit creation to gain those things, we can be sure that we will lack nothing that is needful for us.

This delight, this joy in God that is God's gift to us, brings true fulfilment because it gives us that inward freedom from any dependence upon earthly things and allows us to keep a joyful heart even when deprived of possessions, deprived of health, perhaps with a death sentence over us through cancer or deprived of success when everything had seemed to point towards our being able to achieve what our heart longed for in the service of God. The lesson is that we may have our doubts, our questionings, our fears – but just as the psalmist says at the close of Psalm 4, 'Lord, you alone make me to dwell in safety', so we can surely with even greater assurance echo his words: 'I will lie down and sleep in peace, for you alone, O Lord, make me to live and sleep unafraid.'

Chapter Five
BEREAVEMENT

A number of years ago I was angered and saddened at the funeral of a prominent Christian surgeon where the person officiating beamed as he said: 'Isn't this a glorious occasion?' while the widow and family were openly sobbing and grieving for the premature loss of someone who could not be replaced.

This seemed to me to represent a very inadequate reaction to the complexity of the bereavement situation, and the emotional needs of the bereaved. Bereavement refers to the loss of a significant relative or friend, and in some situations the loss of a grandmother or aunt may be more significant than of a mother, of an uncle, or an elder brother more significant than the loss of a father. It's the significance of the individual rather than the actual relationship in terms of status that is important.

Depression and mourning are very closely related, with the grief of bereavement often having the signs of a particular kind of depression. There are many first-hand accounts of bereavement in literature, both secular and spiritual. In the Bible we have, for example, Job, Naomi, Ruth, David and Martha, and in secular literature people such as C S Lewis, or Dickens' Miss Haversham in *Great Expectations*, jilted and still surrounded by her wedding cake and wedding dress many decades later. One of the most powerful examples is the account of her mother's death by Simone De Beauvoir, which I will come back to later.

Over the centuries the bereavement situation within our culture has been the province of the pastor and I suppose to a large extent this is still so. Most people expect to have somebody to bury them even if they have never seen a minister before, and today I suspect that there are more people buried by clergy than are baptised by clergy. In the past few years medical students have been given special seminars on bereavement, bereavement reactions and how they should deal with them, as they are being expected to deal with bereavement as a medical problem, or at least not to treat it as a taboo subject.

But what does happen at bereavement? Well, the death disrupts a whole series of habits that a couple have built up together and shared and whose abrupt disappearance intensifies the feeling of a gap that cannot be filled. Now whether this couple is husband/wife, parent/child is immaterial. There is a whole series of habits that they have built up together and shared and death causes an abrupt disappearance. It has been traditional to sub-divide the bereavement reaction into stages and durations. There is first the stage of severe distress and turmoil where there is often non-acceptance that the person has died. There may even be a calling upon the dead person as was the case where David cried out, 'O my son Absalom, my son, my son Absalom.' You might get this when a person has died and the relative shakes the person saying, 'Come back to me, come back to me', knowing full well they are dead.

Then a period of numbness takes over and it is during this time that the funeral arrangements and the set ritual and necessities take over. At the funeral there tends to be a release of the emotions. There is a dramatisation of what has happened as the body is lowered into the grave and the soil put on top. In so doing one has enacted visually what one knows has occurred – the person is now gone, buried, departed – and in my view it is highly advantageous for the bereaved person to see that kind of visual representation going on. We will come back to that.

Then there is the period of grief or mourning, which is also a readjustment. People have tried to separate grief and mourning – but I cannot make much sense of the literature that tries to do so – it seems to me that they are not really separable. The grief, the mourning and the readjustment all go on together. There is the brooding over the person, the recalling of events, the experience of old situations without the individual that causes an onrush of new emotions and then a readjustment at the same time. So it is all going on together, the healing and the pain and the anguish meeting it again, and the readjusting. The duration during which this sort of thing happens varies enormously within so-called 'normality'. Some people used to think six weeks and you should be over it. This is sometimes still thought, but my own view is that it takes well over a year for this to happen.

There is a sense in which a bereavement leaves a permanent gap and there is no total recovery because the person has gone. However, one of the earlier studies looking at this went to a Welsh valley and looked at the prescription of anti-depressants and tranquillisers to bereaved people and found that prescribing tended consistently to fall off after 18 months. Some people needed a bit longer, some people didn't need any and some much less, but there was quite a dramatic cut-off as the bereaved person went through the first Christmas, the first New Year, the first birthday, the first anniversary, the first holiday and so on. Having been through the whole season, then came the anniversary and the following year, having been through it all once, the person began to say, 'Yes, this is not new, I am not dreading it in the same way. I remember how I dealt with it last time and it's not quite as frightening.' I have observed among friends of ours who have been bereaved that it was hard work for a year. Then came the first anniversary and something a bit lighter entered the scene and they began to look out a bit more. So I would suggest a period of about 18 months based on psychological and medical studies and my experience.

I would propose, however, that in reality there is no separation of one stage from the other because the numbness may come back from time to time, the distress may come back, the readjustment will be there all going on together and the person may feel intense despair and anguish as they remember some particular incident and feel, 'O dear, I'm right back where I started', though the next day would probably say that the pain was momentary. I like the image of climbing a scree face: you go up two steps and slide down again and then you go up another three steps and go down two. I think it was C S Lewis who used a different analogy, when he likened it to going along a valley bottom and then suddenly you turn a corner and say, 'Oh, I've been here before' and so on.

What about the grief itself? How do we understand it? In my view what is happening here is that all the emotions involved in the process of getting to know the person and building up our relationship with that person during life, are recapitulated in some way in the process of grief, so the more complicated the relationship was in life, the more complicated may be the experience in death. The more problematical the communication during life, the more problematical may be the person's bereavement reaction as they try to disengage and get on with life. But whereas it may have taken years for the relationship to be built up, this other process may take only days or months.

Let me give you an example of someone who for many years was the mistress of a man who remained married with his family and home life. It is unclear if his wife knew what was going on, probably she did but was determined not to enquire too deeply for one reason or another. So this man got all that he considered necessary for affection, love and sexuality from one woman, and from the other he got his domesticity, his children and his partner for official functions. That was the way it was for years, until this man had a heart attack in his mistress's house. She was in a total panic as to what to do, but he got to hospital and died there. What then became of the bereavement situation? Who was the most bereaved? The person whom nobody knew about, who dreaded that he would actually die in her house but who looked upon herself as the person who gave him real affection, love, caring, interest and all that he needed as a person, or the woman who kept his house clean, mothered his children, was his consort at functions and fed him? She was the one who put on the widow's weeds and was the one to whom people sent condolences. She was the one who went to his funeral and she was the one who was able to stop her job for a bit. Whereas the other woman the next day had to get up and at 9 o'clock, be in her office and carry on as though life was normal. Her grief had to be clandestine, as hidden, as unshared, as unsupported as was her relationship with that person in life.

Simone De Beauvoir was the mistress of Jean-Paul Sartre. Some of you may be familiar with her autobiography, which runs into several volumes and in which she was determined to be honest in all her communications, and very honest she was too. But there is a tiny volume entitled *A Very Easy Death* that she did not include in her autobiography. In it are her comments and reflections on her reactions to her mother who was dying of cancer, which she pulled out of her autobiography and published separately. In my view, although she doesn't say so, it was here, on this one bit of her life, that she was unable to be honest. She writes about her relationship with her mother: 'For all that, I was astonished at the violence of my distress. Suddenly there was an outburst of tears that almost degenerated into hysteria, amazement. When my father died I did not cry at all, this time my despair escaped from my control, someone other than myself was weeping within me. I talked to Sartre about my mother's *mouth* as I had seen it that morning and about everything I had interpreted in it: greediness refused, an almost servile humility, hope, distress, loneliness. The loneliness of her death and of her life that didn't want to admit existence. Sartre told me that my own mouth was not obeying me anymore. I had put my mother's mouth on my own face and in spite of myself I copied its movements. Her whole person, her whole being was concentrated there and compassion had rung my heart. In spite of appearances, even when I was holding my mother's hand I was lying to her and because she had always been deceived, gulled, I found this ultimate deception revolting. I was making myself an accomplice of that fate which was misusing her; at the same time, in every cell of my body, I joined in her refusal and in her rebellion.' So she described her mother dying of cancer. She was a good, bourgeois Catholic and here was Simone De Beauvoir who had rejected all that her mother stood for and was now colluding at her mother's death with, 'Oh yes, and you will get better', and all the bourgeois, Catholic denial of cancer and death was going on at that bedside. But she had never been honest with her mother. She had never been able to say to mother, 'I loathe all you stand for with your Catholicism, your bourgeoisie and your denial.' So here in the bereavement situation that she was anticipating was all the tremendous conflict, creating an explosion of emotion that this woman, who prided herself in her Gallic rationality, found herself overwhelmed by. Powerful stuff, and of course people like Simone De Beauvoir are masters of language and can express something that the rest of us find difficult to put into words, but the emotions are the same if we are in the same situation.

C S Lewis wrote *A Grief Observed*, initially published under the pseudonym Clark. Here he was, a bachelor who had felt that love was something that had passed him by. Suddenly in late middle life, he found all the emotions of a teenager welling up within him as he met Joy Davidman and subsequently married her and wrote his *Four Loves*, a magnificent book, full of fun and humour and insight. Then she died and he went through the agonies of 'God, what was all this for? I got used to my singleness and then you gave me this, then you took her from me.' Given that concentrated taste of love in late middle life, suddenly he had a very concentrated, very turbulent bereavement reaction, and when one Christian author and preacher learned that it was C S Lewis who had written the book, he protested that it should never have been written. Nonsense! The book had to be written because it is part of our common human experience.

So what are the kind of emotions that make up those of us who are less verbal than these two individuals? How can we be more specific? First there is fear, the dread of being alone, the butterflies, the suspense, the waiting, the expectation of a moment, of a meeting that will never come. Second, what about depression? It is known that there is an association between loss and depression. This has been known for centuries, but in this feeling of depression a person may say, 'Is it because of me that this person has gone, was I to blame?' One woman whom I saw as a patient spoke of how she helped to kill her father by assisting the doctor as he gave her an injection for the pain of terminal cancer from which he subsequently died. This was not euthanasia, but in her despair and sorrow she said, 'I helped put my father away.' The self-blaming and self-doubt, the mixed emotions, the shame and the guilt and then the suicidal rumination; all they want to do is to be with the dead person. The woman I saw recently said: 'I heard my father's voice saying 'Come home'.'

The depression, the aggression, the blame may be projected elsewhere; 'It's not I who have done this, it's not I who am to blame, it's they, the doctors, her friends, the children, even the dead themselves. If only my husband had listened to me and not spent so much time going round all these parishioners, or all these patients; if only he'd spent more time with us and not spent himself for other people, perhaps he would be here today.' Remember Martha when Jesus came after the death of Lazarus. She said, 'If only you had been here, what's been keeping you, what right have you to withhold yourself in this way.' There may be outbursts of anger, and the anger may be visited on the first person to call: the doctor, the minister or members of the family. The bereaved person may be bitter or resentful, and they may be appalled at the intensity of their feelings when the caller has gone. Then when the fear and depression have passed, suddenly they may be aware that they are relieved that the person has gone, even glad for the sense of release, that this mother, whom they had to nurse for two years, with the sheer physical and mental exhaustion, resentment and conflict associated with their mother's care, has gone. The less able they were to look at those emotions beforehand, the more this may hit them with subsequent guilt and depression. Then may come the symptoms of sleep disturbance, being off one's food, exhaustion, sheer fatigue, butterflies in the stomach.

Most people will come to terms with bereavement in some measure, but problems in coping with bereavement may be shown in subsequent behaviour. For instance, a person may never become profoundly depressed or suicidal, but what happens is that they become housebound. The fear that is part of being bereaved becomes paralysing, dominant and permanent, and agoraphobia may begin after the death of a spouse or more often the loss of a father or mother. Fear can be dominant and crippling, and bind the person at home. The emotions are never completely worked out, the depression can become suicidal, with a preoccupation with death and an identification with the dead person. There may be a seeing of the dead person or hearing their voice. One should watch in particular the first anniversary. One may feel the person is coping with this alright but then they go down quite unexpectedly on the first anniversary. Likewise with the second anniversary, because on the first anniversary somebody might have taken the person away on holiday so that they never really dealt with the loss, whereas the second anniversary may be the first one they spend alone.

A question may be asked about whether a reaction is normal or abnormal and will it be prolonged. In my experience a complex reaction is more common in younger women than other groups. The type of bereavement is also important. Is it unexpected, or caused by suicide? Has the bereavement happened away from home or is it of a child? These are the kinds of bereavement that make a person more vulnerable. If a death occurs in hospital as opposed to at home, there is more chance of an abnormal reaction, and if it happens on the street or away from home, there is a greater chance of such a reaction. A death at home where the bereaved person is secure is more easily accepted.

Let us leave the last word to St Paul who, writing to the church at Thessalonica in chapter 4 of his first letter, perhaps thinking of how the Lord wept over the death of Lazarus, said that whereas Christians grieve a loss they do not grieve as those who have no hope. 'We believe that Jesus died and rose again and …. the dead in Christ will rise.' He concludes, 'Encourage one another with these words.'

Chapter Six
DEPRESSION

One of the criticisms made to me about a psychiatrist's view of depression and other problems in people's lives is that the psychiatrist sees a very biased sample of life and therefore presents a biased account of how to deal with these situations. There may be some justification in this. However, I am an ordinary person as well as a psychiatrist and as I reflect on the vicissitudes of life as they affect me, my family and my friends, I am able to use a few tricks of the trade from my professional background, which I share with you now as it may help others in their own lives or the lives of their friends.

Let me first quote from a thesis that a theological student prepared after spending twelve weeks as a voluntary member of staff in one of the wards in the hospital where I work. He was doing this as his practical placement and decided that rather than seeing an occasional patient, he should become a member of the caring team subject to the same pressures as the other staff, with the same shift system. Afterwards he wrote this: 'I found it quite disturbing to find how normal most of the people on the ward were. They displayed various symptoms which I and my friends might also show at times of stress. Often their thoughts and my thoughts would run along similar lines. In many cases the causal factors of their admission to hospital were similar to the ones which had most or almost engulfed me during life's journey. This aspect was very frightening and threatening. Was I really different from them? Seeing people seemingly caught up in a vicious circle and being trapped like a rabbit caught in a car's headlights caused impatience, frustration and despair to well up inside me, not least when many patients I saw said, 'I never ever thought that this would happen to me'.'

Then he went on to say: 'To see and hear about Christian patients caused me not only discomfort and embarrassment, but also called into question the validity of the Christian experience. Is Christianity really just another neurosis which is substituted for other neuroses less acceptable in the eyes of the world? What did a Christian commitment mean to people who seemed like Christian flotsam and jetsam flung aside and washed up by the ebb and flow of life's torrent? I found that I benefitted more from the situation when I opened up some of my more dogmatically defended ideals and became more vulnerable, for that which is true and valid will stand up to exposure, cross-examination and testing, just as pure gold stands up to the refiner's fire.'

He was a much more lucid writer than I am and from a completely different discipline; so I asked his permission to quote this because I find that it sums up in much more felicitous terms than I could ever do the kind of things that I want to say.

So let me expand. Depression is variable in its manifestations, but only a proportion of people who say they feel depressed ever go to their doctor. A still smaller proportion go to a psychiatrist. Of these, a few may need to go into hospital, but for most of them it is a one-off event, with very few ever needing to be re-admitted.

Why do people become depressed? All of us are subject to the effects of the Fall of Man as it affects our genetics, our family background, our culture and our life experiences, and depression is caused by a mixture of all these factors. Heredity is important and studies on twins show quite clearly that identical twins are more likely to be concordant. By that I mean that if one twin is ill then the other twin is likely to show the same kind of illness. In contrast, non-identical twins tend to show the same pattern as ordinary brothers and sisters, as do studies of twins who are brought up apart.

It is not just genetics that are important but the constitution of the person as well. In certain severe depressions and particularly those depressions that have ups and downs of mood where a person may be elated at times and depressed at other times, there is a strong constitutional tendency. Other factors such as family background, life events and life experiences are also important. For example, the experience of bereavement in later childhood and very early adolescence is associated with a three times greater incidence of depression in early adulthood. It is as though a person is primed to respond in a particular way to subsequent loss situations because they have experienced a fundamental loss that has disturbed their minds at a particular and critical period of development. So when they meet subsequent loss situations, whether that is loss of a relationship, loss of health or any other loss, they are more vulnerable and more likely to become overtly depressed in a way that requires help.

Physical factors are important too. Most of us who have had severe influenza or other viral conditions will know the enormously debilitating effects that produces: lethargy, fatigue, and if there are other, even quite minor, issues going on at the same time, a bit of boyfriend trouble or mother trouble or work trouble, then bang! down goes the individual. After every flu epidemic we see a rush of people coming into hospital with depression.

Age is also important. The older one becomes, the more likely one is to break down and come into hospital. But there is also a peak around the thirties for women. That is when husbands are not always very supportive and wives maybe have got three children round their ankles all under the age of five. It is a tough time. From the age of 50 onwards the graph begins to rise again and keeps on rising. Why should it be in this age group? It may be because it is the time when retirement is approaching or perhaps redundancy, terrible word, with all the associated emotions. It is the time when the children are growing up and getting married, or living with boyfriends and girlfriends when parents may feel they ought to have waited longer. It may be the time when ill-health begins. To personalise this a little bit, I was aware of this even earlier. I remember my fortieth birthday: I was aware of my first twinge of arthritis, my first false tooth, I first had to wear spectacles for close work and first got sunburn on the back of my head. I was suddenly conscious of my mortality. The more invested one is in having a good head of hair, in being athletic, in having a nice row of teeth, the more vulnerable one is when these things begin to disintegrate.

On top of this are cultural factors: some cultures find it easy to express emotion, others find it much more difficult. The Scots I always feel are the most direct of people. They can say what they think and I had to learn when I came to the south-west that here everyone smiles very nicely at you, but my goodness the knives are there under the table! The Welsh weep copiously over everything and as a psychiatrist I would deduct fifty percent of their tears to find out what was really going on. This is the kind of backdrop against which we see depression, and God begins to deal with us with all the complexity of our backgrounds, our genetics, our family events and our life's vicissitudes.

Assessing depression

When a person gets depressed one has to decide if this is somebody who requires special help or whether they may be able to work through it. One person may come to me as a psychiatrist, another goes to their general practitioner and yet another merely goes round to their neighbour for a cup of tea and a chat. How does one decide how serious it is? How does one assess what is really wrong and whether a person needs a doctor or their vicar or a good friend? Is this person just acting out a role, or maybe fundamentally is it a spiritual problem: a lack of meaning and understanding of God's purposes? As a doctor, when I see somebody I have to decide whether to send them to their vicar, or to the GP, or admit them myself directly to hospital. If none of these apply, I may say, 'There is nothing very much wrong with you. What I think you need to do is join x, y, or z, and then get out a bit.' That is the kind of interaction that goes on.

Understanding depression

Let me take it a stage further. The word 'model' is a word that is used frequently in our society and what it really means, as I understand it anyway, is that here is a way of looking at certain phenomena, given certain assumptions. It provides a way in which we can proceed from that particular philosophical, theoretical framework. That is not to say that it is the only way of looking at the problem, but it is one way.

1. The medical model of depression

The first model I use when talking about depression is what I call the medical or organic model. That is to say: here is someone who has an illness. They are sick. Something has gone wrong with their body. Just as any other patient they are in bed with their toes turned up. In other words, there they are flat on their back helpless. 'Do something for me, doctor' is the kind of understanding of that particular model. So if the patient comes feeling, 'Yes, I'm sick, I'm ill', I have an idea that something has gone wrong with the mechanism.   It is beginning to creak and groan because something has happened to it and doctors are trained to look at signs and symptoms, things that have gone wrong, signs we can see and observe. We tap people's knees and scratch their toes and listen to their hearts to hear the things that go wrong. Instead of the heart going bump, bump, it goes bump, bump, bump, bump, or toes instead of going down go up, which tells us there is something happening in that particular locality of the brain. If we do a few more tests, we can zone in a bit further.

Signs and symptoms
Symptoms are what the person feels, but symptoms can be very variable and people can have quite different levels of pain tolerance. Some people are not very good at verbalising what is wrong with them and some people go into meticulous detail and you have to subtract a lot of what they say or take it with a pinch of salt. So the signs are the important things. If the person says 'I'm depressed", I say to them: 'Can you tell me what that feels like?' They might say, 'Oh, I just feel terrible.' So I say: 'What sort of thoughts go through your mind when you get depressed? What is the kind of thing that takes over, no matter how stupid or

irrational it seems?' And that helps them to sharpen a little bit what is going on.

What one is looking out for here from the organic model is thinking that is morbid, that is dominating their lives. The language that we use in medicine is morbid preoccupation. It's not just that they feel a bit fed up and sad and bored and angry and so on, but when they look at things there is a death quality to it. They are thinking of the worst that can happen in a gloomy all-pervasive way. There is a sadness that pervades everything in their life. It is almost as though somebody has got a pot of grey paint, a bit blacker in some people, a bit whiter in others, but it is grey anyway and the whole of life is washed with this grey paint: themselves, their relationships, their work, their capacity and so on. That to me is something that requires further investigation, especially when the way in which they are presenting themselves is not what one would have expected from their life history so far. Here is a person who is successful in business, a person who has apparently coped with family and relationships, a person who people have liked and who now sees themselves as unlikeable, not coping, not functioning and you realise something has happened here. The more you go into things with them, the more they portray everything covered with this grey paint.

One man who came to see me, a highly successful businessman, told me he was absolutely incompetent, his productivity was nil, he was a hopeless husband and a hopeless father. Where this kind of negative or morbid preoccupation is present there are often thoughts of suicide, which must always be taken seriously. We cannot help everyone who threatens suicide, but the person who previously has functioned well and then begins to have morbid preoccupations, who has thoughts of suicide in that context, must be taken very seriously.

Another warning sign is sleep. Here it is not usually the pattern of being unable to get off to sleep, but rather the person who falls asleep and then at two in the morning is wide awake, their guts churning as they think about the day ahead of them, and all the problems of the world seem to crowd into their mind.

There may be a very specific situation, like a move of house, when it becomes a pattern that the things we churn over in the early hours of the morning worry us less later in the day, but if the next morning the thoughts are back again with a vengeance then this is a strong indication that here you are dealing with a depression that should be seen from the organic model.

A third pointer that goes along with this is a diurnal variation of mood where one wakes up in the morning and feels ghastly, but later on in the day things seem to improve and in fact by the evening the person may feel almost back to their old self. The sort of thing that happens to me as a consultant is that the GP will ring up at 11 o'clock in the morning having done his morning rounds and say: 'I've just seen Mrs X. She's in a terrible state. She's agitated, frightfully morbid, suicidal. I really think she ought to come into hospital. She refuses to see anyone, but I think she needs help. Would you please come and see her with me?' So I say: 'I'm fully booked, but I'll come along and meet you at the patient's house at 7.30 this evening.' We turn up in the evening and there she is, as bright as a button, smiling all over, and the GP says: 'She wasn't like that this morning, I can assure you.' It's almost always diagnostic. I ask: 'Is this what it's like?' She says: 'Yes, it's a funny thing. Every morning is terrible. This morning was especially bad because my husband had gone back to work after a holiday and that just made it so much worse.'

Another sign to look out for is appetite. Some people stuff themselves when they are depressed, some people can't eat. Food sticks in their throat. They can't swallow. Their stomach is churning and so on. The person who stuffs themselves when depressed is someone who is doing a self-comforting technique. The one who loses weight is the one to look out for.

Lastly there is what I call retardation. It is a long way of saying the person is slowed up, but it's more than just feeling a bit droopy. This is someone who feels that their mental processes are slowed and their physical processes have slowed, not just on an occasional basis, but gradually over a period of weeks, sometimes months. I remember the bank manager who came and I was told by the GP: 'This is one of the youngest bank managers in his group in the locality, a bright, breezy chap.' In he came and sat down and went into the most meticulous detail, dotting every 'i' several times and crossing every 't'. It was incredibly hard work getting the simplest information out of him and my reaction was, you may be a bank manager, but I wouldn't invest tuppence with you. He said: 'I'm not depressed. I just feel I've got all these problems.' I agreed he did have problems. I put him on an anti-depressant and he came back three weeks later, bouncing in, much more like his usual self. Within five weeks he was back again, and trying to loan me money at a fantastic interest rate. I could see why this chap had got where he was in his profession. He still had his problems and we had to go into them, but to have tried to deal with his problems when he was in a parlous state of mind would have been disastrous and almost was.

So those are the signs and symptoms. That's the medical approach and I'm trained to do that. However, there's no reason why a friend can't do a little checklist. The fact that somebody weeps means nothing. As I said, the Welsh weep, the Scots don't, nor do those among whom I work in the south-west. There is a cultural thing about weeping. Perhaps more significant is the person who says, 'I can't weep. I've lost all tears. I wish I could weep.' So be careful that you are not drawn by the layman's idea of depression.

Causes of depression
Let's go on to causation. There is usually something apart from physical factors, or genetics. There is usually some precipitant that has occurred. The interesting thing is that when you look at the precipitant it is not necessarily any worse than happens to the majority of us. What so often does happen is that there have been two or three things that have all occurred in close proximity. Most of us cope with a bereavement; most of us cope with moving house; most of us cope with a new baby; most of us cope with a broken relationship; most of us cope with new jobs. But when you change house, change job, welcome a new baby and have a bereavement

and then get 'flu on top of it, all in the same year, it's like being in a trench and putting your head up and finding there are five snipers all firing at you from different directions and that is what may trigger depression. The person gets into a state where for one reason or another previous coping strategies no longer work.

Then we come on to pathology and there is considerable evidence that there is an alteration of the brain chemistry in the kind of depression that I have been talking about and particularly in those patients who are depressed and sometimes also have episodes of elation. It is known that the sodium within the cells shoots out into the fluid outside the cells as a person goes up or down and when they go the other way the sodium comes back again. In fact, this is used in certain forms of therapy where the sodium acting in this way is blocked, and although the person is aware of something going on, it does prevent the rapid swings of mood in certain individuals. I have no doubt that there is a chemical change involved. You can argue it is the emotional problem that produces the chemical change but chemical change there is, and that is one of the things we are interested in that provides a rational basis for these kinds of depression.

Doctors are obliged to think in terms of diagnoses and label the patient, which puts people into categories and runs the risk of dealing with them in these categories instead of as people. As a professional, I see perhaps 15 new individuals in the anguish of suffering every week. I've got to have a professional way of handling this, which includes recognising that this is a person who is fundamentally depressed, which I can deal with, and then by giving a diagnosis I am able to communicate with other doctors. I am able to give some kind of idea of prognosis, a way of understanding the condition.

Treatment
Then we come to treatment and one treats according to the kind of diagnosis we have given. There is one treatment for the person whose mood swings up and down. For the person who has a severe agitated depression who becomes almost mute, not eating,

then electro-convulsive-therapy (ECT) is by far and away the best, most life-saving treatment that is in existence and has been for many years. There is nothing wrong with ECT, although there is a lot wrong with the way some people have used it. I have a little trick and sometimes use a video in hospital. There was a patient who came in who was dying because she wasn't eating, she wasn't drinking, she was mute, she was not responding to anything. We made a video of her and she sat there absolutely mute, not moving, and the registrar who was speaking to her during the video said: 'Look, if you can hear and understand what I am saying, would you just raise your left hand, that's all. Just raise your left hand.' Two minutes later, one hand very tentatively went up. She was so preoccupied with her morbid thinking and so retarded that it took that amount of time for the processes of the brain, as it were, to work. She had ECT and three ECTs later she came back for a further video. She marched in, sat down and the doctor said: 'Well, how are you feeling?' 'Terrible, awful, I'm frightfully depressed.' But my goodness, you could feel the difference! And five ECTs later she came back in again, saying: 'Oh, very much better, thank you, doctor. I really do feel I'm almost back to my old self.' Dramatic. I show this to the students. I don't tell them beforehand what the treatment is and they may feel I've conned them. But it's one way of saying: 'Let's beware of our preconceptions and all the rubbish that we read.' *One Flew over the Cuckoo's Nest* is a marvellous film, highly enjoyable, but a travesty of some aspects of what goes on in hospitals and it is not a film upon which to base one's views of ECT.

2. The intrapsychic model

Let's move on now to the intrapsychic model. Here we are looking at the attitude of mind that the individual has about themselves. It's what goes on inside their own head: learning experiences, loss experiences and the whole question of whether they were given approval as children or not. When we go into life, how do we know that we are of any value? One way is by acquiring professional expertise, amassing all the prizes and awards that are possible and lining them up on the mantelpiece saying, 'That's what I'm worth.' There may be nothing wrong with that, but the person who has not also been given self-worth as a child by their parents may be over invested in those gongs and cups and medals and certificates because that is the only way they know how to measure what they are worth. Then when things begin to go wrong in their professional life it is not just their professionalism that is threatened, it is their whole self-esteem that is being attacked.

This idea of giving value and worth to people is something that we should be seeking to do. One of the marvellous words in Scripture is that of encouragement. There is not much said about what fathers should do for their children, but there is one thing that is said very clearly. 'Fathers, don't discourage your children.' Look for ways of encouraging them. Fathers may come in from work saying, 'I'm tired, get out of the way', or 'Children, upstairs', and when the children do something good the father's response is, 'Well, what else do I expect?' How do their children know what they are worth when their parents do not communicate this to them? How do they know if they are loved and valued, despite the weaknesses of which they may be only too well aware? You can start at any stage in life. It doesn't matter if you are 50 and say, 'I wasn't encouraged as a child.' Okay, start now. Look for opportunities to encourage each other, encourage those around you, encourage your children. Even if you are 70 and you have 50-year-old children, you can still start encouraging them, even though you have never done it before. They will take it and probably say: 'Golly! What's happened to him or her.'

Psychopathology
We will not spend too much time on this. Here we are talking about what was written by Jung and is found in many do-it-yourself psychology books. It involves looking at personality types: the person who projects, the person who introjects, the introvert, the extrovert. Whatever particular school of psychology or sociology you are looking at, none of these are wrong, they are merely a framework around which one can order one's thinking.

Psychotherapy and counselling

Then we come to psychotherapy and counselling as part of treatment. I use those terms in the broadest way. They really mean entering into some kind of relationship, a verbal interchange, sometimes non-verbal interchange, between people. That can be as tightly controlled and professionalised as lying on your back in an analyst's room one hour every day, five days a week, for two years and paying the earth for it. That is one approach. It has its value, perhaps, although it is not without its hazards. I think it does help some people in certain contexts. Much more relevant is the counselling approach and that can be anything from the neighbour next door saying: 'There, my dear, have a cup of tea! Let's talk about it. I can't really help you, but anytime you want to come round and have a chat, do just that.' That is counselling. One is making oneself available to somebody: being a paraclete, drawing alongside, comforting, strengthening and upholding, and that is certainly part of what God has given us to be able to give to each other. Let me say that sometimes one does have to set limits on this. The important thing is to recognise what you can offer and what you can go on offering today, tomorrow, next year, if necessary. The problem with many well-meaning Christians can be that they offer more than they can sustain. Then the person keeps on coming round and they are kept to their word but end up saying 'Sorry, not now' and then rightly feel guilty as the person takes this as just one more rejection. It is far better to say, 'That much I know I can give, and keep on giving.' They may demand more so you say, 'I'm sorry.' It is in the consistency of the caring and counselling that you can give that there is something ultimately much more healing than offering unlimited availability that you cannot keep up. I can't emphasise that too strongly.

3. The interpersonal model

Then we come to the interpersonal model. Here I am talking about relationships. All of us are in some kind of relationship with other people. There are people to whom we relate easily and people we would probably choose not to be involved with. Likewise, there are people who would wish to be involved with us and people who might well avoid us. No man is an island and the way in which we react to people may be very different in some contexts from others. We may see older people always as father figures and seek to draw father-like things from them. We may be the sort of people who dislike figures in authority as we see in them paternal authority figures, so we always test them out. We all have our likes and dislikes and we can see something of our backgrounds coming out in this. There are people who we feel warm towards. We become very caring because they draw something from us that gives us something that we need. Or we may approach people saying, 'I am depressed', and we want them to say, 'There, there, we love you all the same', and that makes us feel better.

Sometimes in hospital when a doctor walks into the room and asks, 'How is Mrs X?' The answer comes back, 'She's fine.' And she was fine, chatting and laughing, but as soon as she sees the doctor, down goes the head and the tears come and she's saying: 'I know I'm bright and cheerful with them, but I really think I still need special help from you and don't you dare discharge me from hospital.' That may be an extreme form of manipulation. Most of us would recognise this, but some people can put it on very heavily and keep demanding reassurance again and again. It is impossible to convince them. They will always approach us in this sort of way.

I think of one young vicar who came to me and said that he didn't know why but he was having problems with his elders and churchwardens. As we talked I felt the pressure from this chap to do something for him, to give him lots of approval. I hardly knew him and I said: 'Do you know what you are doing? You are trying to make me into a father figure to give you all the things your dad never gave you.' After a break he came back and said: 'You're right. I can see what I am doing. I'm demanding that these elders give me lots of father things but they can't. They can never give me what my father never gave me.' I replied: 'Yes, they can give you a little bit of what your father never gave you and corporately they can probably give you quite a lot, but the moment you push them to be a replacement for your father, that's when they'll back off.' He went off. A year later we met up again, and he said: 'You know, I went back and spoke about this to my church leaders. They've been marvellous since. I've had more liberty.'

This is the kind of thing that we can feed back to a person. Often such behaviour comes from our own family group dynamics, the way in which we handled each other within our families: a mother who always loved us when we were ill because she was a trained nurse and she knew what to do with hurt knees and sore throats, but wasn't very good at cuddling and showing affection; a father who knew how to reward people who got good results, but didn't know quite what to do with rather thick kids.

Some families communicate with tremendous power. I always think Jewish families are an example here. The Jewish Momma is a strong figure and she keeps her brood just there. A few of you may have seen the film *The Chosen*. It really does give a feel of that, and of the distant remote father. Some Gentile families are not unlike that too and Irish families likewise. Some cultures advocate strong, open relationships, and then you have the upper-crust English family where the children are sent off to boarding school at the age of 6, 7, 8 or, if they're lucky, 13, the idea being that it is far better to entrust the care of your children to other people, schoolmasters, people who are not emotionally involved. This can have a huge effect for good or bad on personality. Those of us who come from slightly different cultures look on this viewpoint as an extraordinary phenomenon, though I'm not saying here that there are not grounds for boarding schools. For some children I think they are the best thing that could happen. At least the children get stable and relatively warm individual care and are in a group situation.

In family group therapy, what we are aiming at is trying to enable those concerned to deal together with what is happening. If you can bring the family together, splendid. Sometimes you can't. Sometimes you can only deal with the family by proxy because one person is miles away, but you can begin to deal with specific situations where they re-enact a kind of role play and then ask: 'Could we have done that differently?'

Within a church fellowship group in particular one may notice these things going on and realise that the needs of the whole house fellowship must be taken into account, not allowing one person to take on the invalid, depressive role within it. We may need to say: 'No, that's enough. Come on. We are all members together in this particular family. You can't dominate the whole scene.' There is a discipline that must be set on their behaviour as in any family. Total acceptance is stuff and nonsense. Acceptance, yes, but within limits. When our children misbehave, one lets them go so far and then we say, 'Right, that's enough.' Not every child responds to that kind of approach. Some do. But security is given by the setting of limits. The child with tantrums whose mother wrings her hands and says: 'What do I do with you?' is creating a rod for her own back and terrible insecurity for the child who finds that they can get exactly what they want by their tantrum. But that's not really what they want. They want to feel secure and loved and they want to know that somebody can lay down boundaries.

4. The existential model

By the existential model I mean people who have not got a meaning for life. They don't know what life is about. I always ask patients: 'What makes life tick for you?' And the answer that comes back so often is: 'Well, the kids, the football team, the job and the wife' in that sort of order. The mothers usually say, 'The kids.' And what happens when the children leave and do things of which you don't approve? What happens when the football team loses or goes out of existence? What happens when you are made redundant? What happens when you are taken over and you become second junior secretary as opposed to company secretary? What happens when you are reorganised within the health service and have to reapply for your own job that you thought that you had for life?

What makes life tick for you? What are your fundamental objectives? Here I am looking for a philosophy of life and I sometimes say to depressed patients: 'Are there other ways of looking at life that make life meaningful, give purpose to life?' Sometimes when I feel this is a major problem in the depression I explore things with the patient and we look at the whole question of faith and so on and sometimes they reject such discussion. Others say: 'Well, maybe I ought to think about that.' Others have sometimes begun to resolve this without any push from me.

What is life about? Now from a Christian point of view I have my own answer and this colours the way I approach life's problems. But as a professional I cannot impose my life view on patients. When I teach Christian medical students and nurses I try to say: 'You must not look at people in just one way.' So many Christians think only in these terms, that if you are right with the Lord, get your Quiet Times right, join a house group, come to the prayer meeting, are prayed over, have a healing session, then all will be fine. Now there is nothing wrong with any one of these things in its proper place and properly understood, but if you give the expectation that that's all that's necessary, then you are doing a disservice to that person. You are reducing that person from a man or woman created in the image of God, to a model that you have created according to a particular philosophy that denies much of the rest of what he is as God has created him.

The same is true of a psychological approach, as in the intrapsychic model, where you put the person on their back, you diagnose their personality, you help them to relive their early experiences in vitro – that is, apart from the situations when they occurred. I remember a person reflecting on psychoanalysis. He was asked by somebody: 'Well, what did it do for you?' He said: 'It's given me tremendous insight into my life. When I was young my father was dying and we all had to go round the house on tiptoe, speaking very quietly.' And the physician who saw him said: 'Well, so what? You're still speaking quietly and standing on tiptoe.' 'Yes', he said, 'but now I do it with insight.'

Moving to the organic model again, the doctor who can only push pills and potions or give ECT is denying the plenitude of what we are. Yet I, as a doctor, must look at the organic model. You, as people involved in a Christian fellowship, must look at the existential model. But even when I have got the person somewhat better with drugs and potions, I may then have to do some very hard work with their marriage and the way the person feels and reacts to life and also force the person to look at the meaning of life. Sometimes I say: 'No. You're getting no tablets. We want to see your wife first and see what is going on there and then we'll think about tablets if that's necessary.' So I would use one or all of these models, majoring in one or another at different times.

Practical advice for the pastor
Professional help
First, know what agencies or other help exists in your parish or nearby. Throughout the country there are mental welfare officers who are based in the local public health and social welfare department. They have a statutory role in caring for the mentally ill in the community and a specific geographical area for which they are responsible. They are only too willing to help and be helped and are usually much more approachable than doctors. Their local 'know how' may be invaluable in helping with a crisis situation, especially in city parishes. Otherwise, you must contact the family doctor, for he is the person who is ultimately concerned with the health of your parishioners. Do not be inveigled by the 'patient' into bypassing the GP because 'he doesn't understand'. He may understand only too well. Many Christian patients wish to keep discussion on a spiritual plane, when the treatment may have to include the exploration of some very earthy emotions and situations. Further, the patient may identify the Christian psychiatrist with the Christian establishment about which he has real problems, with which he is unable to cope or even admit to. The advantages of a Christian psychiatrist are, however, that he is likely to understand and appreciate the patient's background and culture and that may engender greater trust.

Pastoral help

What can the pastor do more directly? Above all, treat the mentally ill as normal people. Their feeling of alienation may be very severe, and the recognition that they are being regarded not with fear or pity but as normal brings great comfort. Further, don't feel that you must give spiritual advice. It may be best to stop giving spiritual counselling altogether. Certainly if the person is actually undergoing treatment in hospital, discussion of spiritual issues may be unproductive and occasionally unhelpful, especially in the acute phases of an illness. At these times the best advice may be to tell the person, who is already feeling guilty about their lack of concentration, to take a break from prayer and Bible study. Attendance at corporate worship is rather different and probably should be encouraged, though not invariably. It seems to me that Anglicans generally and Anglo-Catholics and Roman Catholics in particular are better off here than their Free Church brethren because the liturgy and the emphasis on the sacraments can help to carry the individual through a depressive illness.

3.Specific counselling

Having said all this, some men have an undoubted gift in counselling the mentally ill. Men like Richard Baxter and Samuel Rutherford were famed for their counselling ability and today there is a keen interest in this still. Further, the psychiatrist does not have exclusive rights in this field and it seems to me that although the clergy may learn from the psychiatrist, the Christian church has a far greater heritage and longer experience in counselling afflicted minds than do psychiatrists, and accordingly should seek to rediscover and develop its own special skill rather than slavishly adopting the medical model. But if an attempt at counselling in this sphere is taken up, it should be handled with care. Not all doctors are suited to be psychiatrists, nor are all ministers capable of more than supportive counselling. All of us must recognise our own limitations and guard against a wrong involvement and of being unrealistic in what we can achieve.

Above all, when we find we are continually going over the same ground with an individual or find ourselves being emotionally drained then halt, re-examine the situation and seek help.

Chapter Seven
DEMON POSSESSION AND THE OCCULT

First published in *Churchman* vol 94 no 3 1980

As a psychiatrist I hesitate to enter into this particular debate, where so much of the discussion has been experiential, and where there has been little real thinking by the church. If we compare the great doctrines of the faith that have been hammered out in debate, there has been little similar discussion on this issue. Calvin, of course, was utterly scathing, and dismissed the Roman exorcists with the words, 'All, then, which they babble about their paltry orders is a compound of ignorant and stupid falsehoods.' There seems to be an inevitable polarisation on the theme: one extreme seeing demons in every odd manifestation; the other denying the demonic altogether. The resurgence of interest in exorcism today seems to come from two streams in Christian thinking. The first is from the scholastic theology of medieval Roman Catholicism, which has come down through an Anglo-Catholic tradition to us today. The second stems from the charismatic renewal, with its emphasis on certain gifts of the Spirit.

Let me begin my own treatment by looking at the biblical words that relate to our theme. First of all, translations tend to carry very different connotations to different generations. Canon Stafford Wright has pointed this out, and describes how the Hebrew word *ob* was translated as 'familiar spirit' in the Authorised Version, when the translators were contaminated by contemporary sixteenth- and seventeenth-century preoccupation with witchcraft and familiar spirits. The true translation of 'mediumship' was not discovered until the nineteenth century. One relevant biblical word is *ekballo,* which is translated as 'cast out' and should not be translated as 'exorcise'. In fact, the Greek word *exhorkizo* seems to have been deliberately avoided. The other word is *daimonizomai,* which can be translated as 'demonized' and not 'possessed'. This word seems to mean something to do with bondage. With us, 'exorcise' often conjures up the image of bell, book and candle or of special exorcisms. Likewise, the word 'possession' carries with it the idea of control being lost, or of someone being under the influence of another. In my view there are many types of demonised situations, all resulting from the fall of man and all reflecting in some measure the continuing activity of Satan upon us and the world.

Nor does it seem to me that possession and lunacy are clearly differentiated in Scripture. Matthew 4:24 apparently differentiates between those who are lunatic (moon-struck) and those who are demonised. Yet all individuals are included in the term 'healed', since the verse speaks of their various diseases and pains, and of demoniacs, epileptics and paralytics being healed. Similarly, in Luke 7:21-3 there is again an *apparent* differentiation. However, when referring to his actions as proof to John, Jesus omits mention of evil spirits. I cannot, therefore, see these as mutually exclusive categories of 'afflictions', to use Matthew's word. It would appear that they are not to be dealt with any differently from other afflictions. Only in the reference to the confrontation with the demonic, and the episode concerning the Gerasene swine in Mark 5:15, do we find demons and madness being referred to the same person. Even here they are not necessarily equated: it may be that Christ is in direct confrontation with the powers of Satan and in that confrontation there is an affecting of other animate creatures with Satan's destructive influence. Certainly there do not seem to be any distinctive categories of symptoms or syndromes implied in this particular account.

If we turn to other Gospel instances, we find that there are individuals who are specifically mentioned as demonised but that a wide range of disorders is identified. Sometimes they are worshippers in the synagogue, sometimes blasphemers; at other times they are epileptic, blind, sick, deformed, etc. Sometimes nothing is said: at other times sins are forgiven. It seems, therefore, that there is no clear pattern of occurrences, signs or handling of the demonised individual by Jesus. There is nothing here to enable us to distinguish the special marks of Satan and of the demonic that require special handling. There are no distinguishing movements, voices or bizarre behaviour identified. The individuals spoken of as demonised were afflicted: some were sane, some were sick; others were mad, blasphemers or worshippers. All exhibit the activity and effect of Satan in this fallen world. All express the power of Christ over every manifestation. All declare the power of Christ's heavenly majesty over the infernal majesty of Satan (C S Lewis). Accordingly, I think there is a great danger in going further than the Gospels and the epistles. In fact, the epistles are remarkably silent on this whole theme.

Contemporary interest
It may be that, in looking for the marks of demon-possession and in becoming preoccupied with the demonic, we are in danger of being contaminated by the pagan culture around us. There is also a danger in looking for identification signs of demon-possession that, in a former generation, would have been interpreted as signs of spirituality and vice versa. Speaking in unknown tongues was an evidence of demon-possession in the Roman writings. At the same time, the current special interest in demon-possession may well be a reaction to the denial of the spiritual world, rather than the activity of Satan and his powers in our contemporary generation. Helmut Thielicke comments that Satan desires anonymity and C S Lewis says that Satan cannot stand being laughed at. And so it may be that Satan's answer to this is to produce a spirit of fear in many today. In the accounts of those associated with exorcism, there certainly seems to be an underlying spirit of fear and morbid preoccupation in their reaction. However, neither denial nor fearful preoccupation is an

attitude that is inculcated by the New Testament. Rather it is to recognise Satan's power and to rejoice in his defeat as a result of the cross.

In recent years there have been certain books that have been highly influential among Christians, and also some dramatic cases that have focused attention upon demon-possession and exorcism. In particular, Doreen Irvine's and Kurt Koch's books have had a wide circulation, although it is difficult to evaluate their psychiatric data. Koch is neither a medical person nor a psychiatrist. It is all very well quoting medical colleagues but it would have been more credible if his colleagues had written their own chapter. In so far as I am able to evaluate the data as a psychiatrist, I find it very unconvincing. On the other side, the Barnsley case was a very disturbing incident. Here was a man who, it was claimed, had been made mad by a charismatic group. However, he was already a disturbed individual and there was evidence of marital difficulties. Shortly afterwards, there was another case of a child murderer who made a plea of defence that he had been dabbling in magic and spiritism and accordingly felt possessed when he committed the crime. It was subsequently shown during the trial that this particular plea was suggested by the Barnsley case, that the defendant was deliberately lying, and that he had a very pathological personality previously. The theme underlying these particular cases was that demon-possession implied the removal of personal responsibility. The last vestige of restraint was gone, and hatred, murder and insanity were seen by the individual as demonic embodiments. This, of course, is the view taken by certain individuals who are particularly concerned with possession and exorcism. In a strange way, the hyper-supernaturalist and the anti-supernaturalist both seem to do the same thing. For both, responsibility for certain behaviour and attitudes is not with the individual but is seen either as demonic activity or as a result of one's upbringing and society generally. For both, there is a deep personification of the individual. In both, personal accountability is denied or the moral aspect of an individual's behaviour is projected either onto demons or onto society. Having identified a factor, both these approaches then claim that this factor automatically explains the phenomena.

Case studies

There have not been many psychiatric studies and assessments of possession and the occult. However, as Jean Lhermitte says:

'Whether we like it or not, the introduction of Freudian psycho-analysis into contemporary thought has spread, in the last few decades, to all sectors in which the mind is specially concerned. And if one can no longer imagine any literary or artistic criticism, biography or hagiography, without references to the doctrine of the sage of Vienna, one need not be surprised to learn that not even the devil has escaped the clutches of the psycho-analyst.'

For Freud the devil was nothing but the incarnation of psychological repressions. Some modem psychiatrists, such as Sargant, see all so-called spiritual phenomena as merely due to suggestion; this is a view of some very respected and otherwise open-minded psychiatrists. Clinical studies, however, have been few. In 1966, Professor Yap studied 66 cases of individuals in Hong Kong who believed they were possessed either by gods or demons. The cases were predominantly women of rather limited intelligence and mediums and he identified three groups of individuals. The first group he called neurotic. In these, he claimed that the spirit-possession was a dramatisation of the fantasies and wish-fulfilments of individuals who had existing conflicts in their personal lives. The second group were clearly depressed and here the demons were their own voices talking about their sexual and morbid themes. This particular group responded well to physical methods of treatment such as electro-convulsive therapy. The third group were clearly insane. No one accepted them as demon-possessed, and even those people who would certainly have looked upon demon-possession as a way of understanding certain phenomena saw these individuals as undoubtedly mad. They were individuals who seemed to be merely picking up cultural expressions to express their own insane delusions. Yap's comment was that the group who claimed to be god-possessed were looking for some elevation of status, whereas those who were demon-possessed in their own minds were asking for some suspension of criticism from themselves and from others in their state of conflict or depression. Professor Yap was a Chinese trained in the West and was, of course, examining the phenomena he observed according to the canons of Western and materialist medicine.

The French psychiatrist Jean Lhermitte, on the other hand, was an orthodox Roman Catholic who was trying to operate as a believer and an exponent of the scholastic theology of the Roman Catholic Church. In an article he states: 'Our knowledge of mental disorders began greatly to improve from the time when spiritual disturbance ceased to be regarded purely as an expression of supernatural influence and was seen as evidence of modifications in the development of the adjustment of psycho-physiological functions. There is no psychiatrist today who could not with the greatest ease discover under the mask of witchcraft in the past, the most significant symptoms of psychoses such as come up for treatment every day.'

He then went on to show that the natural history of those of his patients who claimed to be demon-possessed was the same as other individuals who did not claim to be demon-possessed but had recognised mental illnesses. He called these people pseudo-possessed. This particular category enabled him to treat them as mentally ill without recourse to exorcism, and also without incurring the censure of Roman Catholic theologians. In his own group of cases, men were just as common as women. All tended to be of high intelligence, had moral difficulties, and saw themselves possessed not so much by spirits as by Satan himself. His material, of course, may well have reflected the fact that he was a good Catholic operating a private practice.

Recently, a junior colleague and I reviewed 20 patients who claimed that they were possessed and had to be admitted to a psychiatric hospital. Some of these patients were clearly schizophrenic: they had shown symptoms of the illness before they claimed to be possessed, and they responded to appropriate medication. Others were clearly profoundly depressed, with a family history of depression, and were also responding well to electro-convulsive therapy. Often the improvement was dramatic. Others showed quite severe personality difficulties and problems within their lives. The average age was 22, and they tended to be highly intelligent, with some kind of Christian background. A high proportion had been in contact with charismatic groups. A number had had the idea suggested to them that they were possessed. Some had received exorcism; one on three occasions. All had considerable sexual conflicts and trauma. Most had problematic homes, where the predominant theme was one of arbitrariness in the parents' attitude towards them. They considered that their parents were inconsistent in their behaviour, and certainly the homes were ones that seemed to lack security. Many had no contact with occultism itself, but those who did have any contact with the occult tended to show an escalation in their behaviour from Ouija boards to deep involvement in magic. All individuals had been searching for guidelines, control, security and meaning for their future and for their forming of relationships. All were looking for some *external* explanation for their difficulties. In all of them reason seemed to be suspended. In some there appeared to be a curious blend of half beliefs. They would pray on the one hand and practice Ouija on the other. Some had an incredible array of bits and pieces from many religions and cults put together. Others seemed to need to make up their own religion as a way of coping with life. The attraction of the occult and of possession as an explanation of individual difficulties would appear to be that in this way, the search for solutions can be given up and responsibility handed over to the demons and to the exorcist. All further conflict and distress can then be looked upon as the fault of the demon.

Conclusions

How can we summarise? It seems to me that the biblical words may well have been misunderstood and mistranslated. Who is to say that we have a complete understanding of these particular words? Furthermore, the Old Testament says that we are to have nothing to do with the occult, and the New Testament allusions do not fall within our health and illness categories. Neither the Old nor the New Testament gives guidelines for spotting demons. Both indicate that God and Christ are more powerful. The epistles give no instructions on identifying or casting out demons, but plenty on Satan's activity in our lives. Helmut Thielicke has a useful section on Satan as diabolos, who is the accuser and tempter. The accuser and tempter both appeal to weakness that exists in us. As with Eve and Job, the accuser was certain that he had some point of vantage in them; yet that point of vantage was still under the restraint of God. So even when a person was delivered to Satan, it was a withdrawal of God's control and restraint of Satan that was taking place. It is because we have sin within us that we give the devil and his minions claim upon us. It is because we have sin within us that he can appeal to it, and it is at this point that God comes to us and says: 'You who are a murderer in your heart, you shall not kill.' So we remember the lies and wiles of the evil one, and call upon the Lord, our Strength and our Redeemer. Accordingly, the projection of our sinfulness onto Satan is not biblical. The demonomorphisation of murder, insanity and blasphemy is not a New Testament concept, but an erroneous view of man and of the Fall. We may be oppressed, troubled, afflicted, tempted and demonised in a dozen ways. We may even be trapped in bondage, but we are not controlled or possessed outside our will. The biblical message is that Christ is Lord. Our call is to repentance and public admission of that, followed by a declaration of deliverance.

The medical material indicates that there are those who are ill and require medical treatment, often electro-convulsive therapy and other psychological help, whether or not they have been dabbling in the occult. We cannot refuse to treat them merely because they have brought their ills upon themselves in certain instances. When a conflict situation is highlighted, special counselling or psychotherapy may be necessary to expose these difficulties and help the individual. In the case of the individual who has been dabbling in the occult, we may use psychological treatment to bring him back into a way of functioning again, and to enable him to reharness his own resources, defences and will. But medical explanations can never be used as reductionist explanations. We know that certain mystical exercises can enable a person to experience God as life-force. This kind of situation occurs in many religions. Likewise, it may be that a deliberate seeking of Satan and of evil spirits exposes the individual to a level of awareness of the satanic that is equally explosive and mindblowing. Accordingly, in the individual who has become mentally upset in association with dabbling with the occult, medical treatment may be necessary to enable that person to cope with life again. Certain counselling and caring may be necessary to establish confidence, trust and understanding. But I do not see any evidence in the New Testament to suggest we should seek for signs of possession. We should never suggest that a person is possessed; and I am as wary as Calvin of the breed of exorcists, of whatever origin. Under no circumstances should we allow the removal of responsibility from an individual. Where special help and counselling are required because of involvement with the occult, this should be within the fellowship of the church. Any charisma of healing should be seen in relation to all the other charismata. If a special service is requested, it should be in public, and associated with repentance and a declaration that Jesus is Lord. When reading the biographies of missionaries, particularly in the Far East, I was always struck by the fact that when the old spirit-worshipper became a Christian after being involved in mediumship and many other occult practices, he burnt his idols, declared in public what he had done and his belief in Christ, and then turned to praise Jesus Christ who was more powerful than the demons.

ISSUES IN THE WORKPLACE

Chapter Eight
THE CONFLICTING DEMANDS
OF WORK AND FAMILY

William Osler, one of the four founding fathers of the Johns Hopkins hospital in Baltimore and the most famous physician of his day, initially emphasised the importance of work over family, saying in a lecture to medical students: 'What about the wife and babies, if you have them? Leave them! Heavy as are your responsibilities to those nearest and dearest, they are outweighed by the responsibilities to yourself, to the profession, and to the public....your wife will be glad to bear her share in the sacrifice you make.'

Those words were written at the height of his career. However, he himself became worn out with overwork and when he was offered the Regius chair of medicine in Oxford at the close of his career in 1904, his wife, who saw how stressed he had become, said, 'Do not procrastinate, accept at once.' He later modified his views presumably based on his personal experience saying: 'I would warn you against the trials of the day soon to come to some of you – the day of large and successful practice. Engrossed late and soon in professional cares, getting and spending, you may so lay waste your powers that you may find, too late, with hearts given away, that there is no place in your habit-stricken souls for those gentler influences which make life worth living.'

Stress has become one of the watchwords of our generation. Books and programmes deal with it, and most GPs' surgeries and psychiatrists' consulting rooms have pamphlets or seminars on how to deal with stress and overcome it, often with stress counsellors on hand to help. Yet stress is not all bad, A book entitled *The Joy of Stress* shows that stress can be useful to people.

Many work better when under a certain amount of stress for it focuses minds and attention. Many in executive positions have known about stress for some time, but it is the open-ended nature of some professions (doctors, clergy, teachers) that adds to stress. When working on multiple sites, with great expectations placed on each, the more conscientious one is, the more difficult it is to avoid stress.

Twenty percent of teachers and ten percent of doctors who retire before the age of 60 do so because of ill health. Burnout has been well known in the mental health professions. There comes a time when there is no more to give out. In 1993 a Tavistock study looked at the mental health and stress levels in young doctors. Alan Johnson, Professor of Surgery in Sheffield, circulated 1,000 surgeons through the Association of Surgeons of Great Britain and Ireland, asking if they felt under stress, and then carried out a second study three years later to identify those areas of stress in a more personal way. In Alan Johnson's survey of 1990, 66 percent of 1,000 surgeons completed the postal survey but in 1993 only 33 percent replied, possibly because of the more personal nature of the questions, which this time asked for reflection on feelings and reactions to certain problems that created stress. What came out was that conflict was at the heart of stress symptoms: conflict between the demands of committees, administration, clinical work and the needs of family and home. Most doctors felt they were able to cope with stress, but they were often bad at weighing up and prioritising the opposing demands between personal and professional issues, between work and home, and that caused conflict.

Society has changed and today the patients' charter, the press, politicians, insurers, lawyers and managers all add to stress levels. Expectations are increased. The image of the doctor as a father figure has changed. Issues that were just below the surface have been brought out into the open. The questions being asked are: What is our personal motivation? What is it that we hoped to do? What ambitions did we have when embarking on medicine as a career? What personal commitment do we really have and have those issues been worked out with regards to spouse and family?

What is it that makes life tick? What is one's motivation in terms of married life? What is happening with family issues? How does one manage time? In the vocational professions why does a person choose to become a doctor, a lawyer, a nurse or a bank manager? Why does a person choose this profession or this speciality?

In medicine a surgeon may be stereotyped as a person who enjoys a certain status, enjoys the financial rewards and likes technical things. A psychiatrist may like helping people, but also enjoy being a curious voyeur. The game of 'Careers' touches on some of these issues, when the players have to choose how much wealth or fame or happiness they want.

Research on the profile of surgeons shows them to be people of self-confidence, authoritarian, intolerant of ambiguity. The average surgeon needs to be in control, strong and resilient. But in the new NHS, managers and budgets come into play and the surgeon has lost much of the control he once had. He is told if he can operate or if he has to wait until next year. They become thwarted, lose control and there is conflict between what they want to do and the reality of the job as it now is. The profile of psychiatrists (and maybe GPs) is that they can tolerate ambiguity, are less authoritarian and patient contact is important to them. But when other people including lawyers tell psychiatrists what they can do, irritation rises, frustration grows and the real job is bypassed.

What do we do when we get frustrated like that? We go for the things that bring gratification. The surgeons do another operation. The psychiatrists see an extra patient or two. One GP took up acupuncture, which let him spend more time with patients while sticking needles into them and letting them talk. Here is a situation he could control with more work and less committees. The frustration is buried in the clinical need for more patient contact. Being overworked, underloved and unappreciated leads to being overwhelmed. Motivation eroded leads to disillusionment. Stress symptoms develop when we no longer see the rewards for which we hoped.

Family life

Many people including burglars go off to their jobs without telling their spouse where they are going. Likewise they come back and do not talk about what they have done. Many doctors go off to work and then bring it all back home. Osler told his students what a privilege it was to be in medicine, suggesting they should leave aside the demands of wives and babies, who would only thank them for the good they were doing for humanity. He later changed his views.

I used to see more wives of male doctors than male doctors themselves. This is beginning to change. I now see more male doctors whose wives have left them and have become depressed. A man marries a competent wife who is then taken for granted by her husband and becomes resentful and neglected and looks after the children on her own. The husband is engrossed in private practice, the weekends go by, he never gets to the parents' evening, or the children's sports day or the carol concerts. The husband takes comfort in the ward or theatre sister while the grieving, bitter, abandoned wife, often with her own profession and career, seeks comfort elsewhere. Today, women in medicine if married are more likely to work out priorities and are better at managing conflicting priorities, often working part-time or job-sharing. Medical marriages are subject to the same pressures as other professional marriages, but when the patients' needs are pitted against family needs, patients often win.

Clergy marriages are similar and the parishioners often win against the family, causing one clergy wife to say, 'Everyone here has a priest except me.' In Alan Johnson's survey of surgeons, when there was a conflict between professional issues and family, the conflict was resolved to the benefit of the profession in 90 percent of cases. Medical men are often remote, inaccessible and unresponsive to distress in the family. Doctor means carer, but often such expectations fail within the family. The reaction of one doctor whose wife was depressed and needed support and comfort was, 'I can't be her therapist.'

There is very little in behavioural science courses on the family life of doctors. Only once in my career was any advice along these lines given, by a Professor of Anatomy who said, 'Ladies and gentlemen, you can do a good year's work in 11 months but never in 12.' Many doctors do not take their whole holiday, which says that family life is a low priority in their estimation. Is there a time of the day when the whole family sits down to a meal together? One surgeon after a conference decided to sit down once a week on Sunday evenings and make the meal a celebration, except when he was on call! One needs time, involvement and personal investment in family. One needs a formula that is kept to, agreed and often revised. Time relaxing and doing nothing might not be what the family would consider 'quality time', which may be altogether more demanding.

One surgeon came home irritable, edgy and bossy and his son said: 'Dad, stop it, you're not in theatre now!' We may come home carrying our work with us, expecting the family to invest in us rather than us investing in them. In one seminar when I was discussing this issue the women were complaining that while their husbands had clinical work to attend to, they were expected to make all the concessions. One said, 'I also have letters to write, but I have to collect the children first.'

The single doctor, especially if she is a woman, has a higher morbidity and suicide rate. I was once on a committee where a woman and a man were up for same job and there was nothing to choose between them. The committee was divided and the chairman asked, 'Who needs the job most?' and decided it was the married man with children. I disagreed and pointed out that he take his support structures with him, whereas the single woman needs to find new a job, new home and new friends. Life may be tough for the single person, who (whether male of female) has no one else with whom to share the domestic chores. In medicine the single person with no family is often thought to be able to spend more time on call during school holidays. Single people need to cultivate interests and work harder with relationships. They can be drawn into overwork and if work does not produce what they expect, disillusionment sets in.

One senior academic who became severely depressed, but came through it, said, 'This has been the most therapeutic experience of my life, although I would not like to repeat it, thank you.' It had made him look at his priorities. May I remind you again that William Osler later in life wrote: 'I warn you against the day of large and successful practice when you will be engrossed late and soon in professional cares – getting and spending. You may find too late that there is no place in your habit-stricken souls for those gentler influences that make life worth living.'

How far you will go in terms of house, home, lifestyle and job depends on your ability, your personality and your spouse, but let us remember that 'Where your treasure is there will your heart be also.' When we are really stressed, maybe after we have destroyed something in our lives, we will be faced with where our priorities really lie. We need to learn how to say no. David Llewellyn MP, in an open letter to a new MP wrote: 'Whatever success you have achieved, if it is at the expense of your wife, family, home or conscience, it will turn to dust and ashes in your mouth.'

Chapter Nine
MASTER OR SLAVE OF TIME

Time is often thought of as the great enemy. None of us seems to have enough of it. When a group of psychiatric trainees filled in a questionnaire, all but two said they felt stressed by the pressure of time. Yet time is the same since time began, a valuable commodity to be handled aright.

Two words in Greek are used to signify time: *chronos* and *kairos*. *Chronos* is the linear progression, relentless and inexorable, which goes on from day to day. When we are older things take longer but we develop strategies to cope, shortcuts learned from the experience of many years. *Kairos* relates to crisis or opportunity, decision time.

One Christian writer has stated: 'Time is, next to grace, the most precious gift of God.' We are therefore neither master nor slave of time. The Christian is the servant of his master, Christ, and it is Christ who is the creator and Lord of time. Therefore we are the stewards of one of God's gifts. Time is God's property.

In the Old Testament the creation story bears witness to this. Lest we retain any illusions and are tempted still to be slaves of time the fourth commandment reminds us that however pressed we may be, the seventh day is the Lord's. The commandments begin: 'I am the Lord your God who brought you out of the land of slavery.' It goes on to tell us that six days we should labour and do all our work but the seventh day we should rest. This commandment reminds us that we are freed from the slavery to time and work. Yet how often we allow our work to spread into seven days a week as though God can rest, but we cannot.

If we study the concept of time in the Bible, we see that scripture is little interested in clock time but rather more interested in times of opportunity. Indeed the New Testament word most frequently translated as 'time', is the word that signifies moments and seasons of opportunity and crisis. This word *Kairos* signifies those moments of time when choices, decisions and actions are presented and taken. The New Testament emphasises that although all creation is spoiled and consequently we may feel the pressures of time, nevertheless Christ has entered into time and redeemed time. Accordingly, we who are reconciled to Christ and live by faith, join with him in redeeming the time (Ephesians 5: 16) and do not live our lives as its slaves and puppets.

It is pagan, therefore, to see time as an enemy. It is sub-Christian to be oppressed by time. It is as a result of our fallen natures that we allow time to afflict us, to pressure us and burden us. Scripture instructs us that we are freed from the view of time that sees man as a victim of a relentless tide carrying him along. Scripture encourages us to have a sensible view and use of time, as the context in which we work and live our lives in the service of Christ. Paul speaks of our 'taking the time (or opportunity) to do good to all men, especially those of the household of faith.' (Galatians 6:10). He encourages us to conduct ourselves wisely, making the most of the times and opportunities, (Colossians 4:5). And again he states: 'we should redeem the time because the days are evil' (Ephesians 5:16). Perhaps the analogy can be used that to pack our days so full that we lose any sight of time being ours to use in his service is an abuse of time in the same way as overfilling our bellies is an abuse of food.

How then do we approach this question of sorting out priorities in the use of our time? Paul encourages us to remember that we are born 'to do those good works which God planned for us to do' (Ephesians 2:10). Christ himself had a very keen sense of timing in his ministry. One author has stated: 'His calendar was arranged. His sole concern on earth was to fulfil the work given to him to do, in the allotted hours.' Indeed Christ reminded his disciples on one occasion, 'Are there not twelve hours in the day?' (John 11:9). Time is therefore ours, to be exchanged for certain occupations and activities, important or otherwise. We must therefore find some hierarchy, some structure, which enables us to do this effectively.

We all have the same amount of time, although we may have different gifts in the capacity to use it. Even so, we must all learn to stop the leaks, concentrate on the job in hand, plan, examine our motives, and then trust Christ for the result. So often, however, the overburdened servant of Christ is trying to impress his Master, so that he can almost be suspected of trying to earn his salvation. Often he seems to enjoy the silent sweet grudge of martyrdom. Sometimes he is simply carnal, living for lots of personal gratification from his multitudinous activities.

In the last analysis, for the Christian all time is God's. Christ is the goal of all our times and opportunities. For any Christian it is a mockery of Christ if we make His service an excuse for our burden of overwork and sense of pressured time.

Career and lifestyle

I wish now to look at those aspects of the life of doctors in particular that seem to me to cause special conflict. First is career and lifestyle. We ought to ask ourselves from time to time what are our motivations in being doctors. In answering that, we may sometimes find a clue as to why we habitually get drawn into activities or pursue certain paths within our career that seem to eat up an inordinate amount of our time. Medicine is a seductive career. We are so clearly meeting a need as doctors that we rarely ask ourselves what other motivations may be present. All of us in caring or healing professions have a need to be needed in our work and the more neurotic that need, the more compulsive may be our need to be swamped by clinical demands.

Furthermore, medicine still offers great opportunities in most countries for acquiring status, position and power. In a television programme a few years ago the producer sought the opinion of some medical students as to why they entered medicine. A large number of them quite unashamedly stated that they saw medicine as a way in which they could acquire fame and money. Now while these may not have been the primary motivations for a Christian going into medicine, when the prospect of these is apparent, the Christian may be gently lured along ultimately at a terrible cost.

There is also a kind of Christian instruction that suggests that the Christian medical student and the Christian doctor should excel in effort, keenness and publications. But not all Christians are excellent in their work. Indeed many of us may be quite average, perhaps even mediocre in our abilities and potential. Oliver Barclay in his book *Developing a Christian Mind* (he himself was intimately acquainted with Christian doctors and scientists over several decades) has written: 'not many Christians rise to the very top of their occupations. They have instead a way of forming a solid backbone in their profession or business. When they are found among the leaders, especially in medicine and science where some have been quite outstanding, it is often due to the originality of their thinking rather than to sheer overwork. But it is because they often provide a reliable core in their profession or business and in so doing, do much to shape its ideals and codes of practice, that Christians have often been more influential than they may realise. The fact that they have not established for themselves an international reputation, often much sought after by their colleagues, is something they are happy to accept where such a position can be reached only by making an idol of one's work. Neither money nor personal success are the things they live for.' There must be limitations for the Christian in his commitment to his profession of medicine. The plaudits of the profession and the praise of patients must never become paramount in our thinking.

While on this theme it is worth referring to our money and lifestyle. Benjamin Franklin once said, 'Time is money.' But I think one can reverse that statement and say 'Money buys time.' Undoubtedly as doctors we are among the higher wage earners in our society. We can spend our time increasing our salaries, either directly by our private practice, or indirectly by our publications and seniority within the profession. Within evangelical biography there are two extremes in the handling of money. There are those who have earned large sums and have given away large sums. There are others who have inherited large sums and given it all away and lived by faith, which in the last resort means receiving from the earnings of other Christians. Both patterns have been an inspiration to many Christians to think and act seriously regarding their money.

However, if we keep to our theme of money buying time, there are two thoughts that I would like to lay before you. We can use our relative wealth to purchase those things that will free us to make ourselves more available to others and also give special facilities to others in our service of Christ. For instance, when it comes to the kind of homes we live in, in the United Kingdom there was a tradition of some Christian consultants living in large houses in the centre of the cities near the medical schools. Accordingly, generations of medical students could gather there for Christian instruction, fellowship and encouragement, and the Christian Medical Fellowship UK derived an enormous amount from just such a tradition in the past. Such homes are now costly to buy and run, and unaffordable to many, although those senior Christian doctors who still can do this and are prepared to open their houses to others have left a great legacy to many students and young doctors who have appreciated their hospitality.

There is still a need for us to think about the kind of homes we purchase and where we purchase them, so that the Christian gift of hospitality can continue to be exercised. Furthermore, do we as doctors need two incomes as a rule? I am aware that many spouses of doctors feel they must have their own career, but I would ask: must it be a wage-earning career? I may be accused of making some spouses feel guilty, but again, where both partners are engaged in wage earning, the time available for others and for hospitality must be severely limited. But let me put a little balance into this. I think it is also necessary that those of us who are giving ourselves in a very exposed way to other people, which must be the lot of most doctors, do ourselves need to guard our privacy. We need to have times that are clearly set aside for refreshment and recuperation. Again, money can buy the time for this and a place where it can be carried out. I am reminded of one well-known Christian preacher who used to love spending the occasional morning in bed, not getting up until midday. He disarmed his would-be critics by stating: I am 'looking after the Lord's servant'.

Family life

Another reasonable call upon our time for those of us who have spouses and families is our family life. Paul writing to Timothy in 1 Tim. 5:8 said that the person who did not provide for their family was worse than an unbeliever. Our families need to know, feel and experience that we care for them as well as our patients. We speak of spending time with our patients so that the patients know that we care for them and take them seriously. Can that be less true for our families? Hopefully we make an effort to turn up on time for our clinics, our ward rounds, our teaching and our committees. Do we make the same effort to have a clearly allocated time each day for our spouse and families, and then to make sure that we are on time? How many of us have one time in the day when we meet together as a whole family to discuss, talk, chat, argue and encourage one another? How many of us have one time in the *week* when we meet together in that way? I doubt if our clinical teams or our academic departments would function if we merely fitted in our ward rounds or the meeting with our colleagues when we happened to have a spare moment.

No doubt our spouses are protective of us and resourceful with regards to the family, but from my experience in trying to help the families of doctors, I was not surprised by a paper a few years ago that drew attention to the high suicide rates among doctors' wives. The suicide rate was four and a half times that for women of the same age. These days when authority within family structure is denied, when the whole pattern of family life is under attack, Christians are called to be counter-cultural, demonstrating an alternative pattern from the disruption of relationships and family structures increasingly prevalent in society. This may mean that extra time has to be given by the Christian doctor to his family at the expense of his career advancement and his status within the profession. Some formula must be found for our families where they feel that they are reasonably compensated for our enforced absences and unsocial hours. And it must be a formula that the family accepts as valid and which is predictable.

Equally important is the time spent by the doctor sharing the personal pursuits of the family. He should have interests outside his work. How can his family see him as a person who cares for them unless he has personal interests that he can share with them? Many doctors have no interests, no activities and no hobbies, only their work. They give themselves no opportunity of enjoying God's world. This puts a limitation especially upon their contact with their adolescent children, for these sons and daughters then have no opportunity to identify with their father as a person. They see Dad only as a work machine, a provider, unable to identify with them. They never see him as a man, relaxed, enjoying life and enthusing about something that they share together. So often, when the adolescent goes through his rebelling phase and begins to push Father a bit and test out his authority, the adolescent has no way of separating the man from his professional values. So his rebellion is against all that Father holds dearest, which may be his Christian profession. Our children need our time and our involvement. They need time with us that is theirs and is secure and sacrosanct. The same is true for the mother who is a doctor. But in my experience women are more able to work out their priorities here, though not without extreme soul-searching in the face of pressure from professional colleagues.

Spiritual life

Let me now turn to time spent in the spiritual care of the doctor. There is an enormous amount of camaraderie in medicine with a sense of common purpose and excitement. No other professional trainees at university go right through from the first to the final year with the same group of people, dissecting the same bodies, attending the same clinics and continuing in such close and constant contact. After graduating, the temporariness of each job, often with frequent changes of hospital, and the sheer pressure of work, lead to a loosening of bonds within the Christian fellowship. The kind of comment that many doctors make is, 'Even if I am able to get down to Bible study and worship, I am not here long enough to put down roots in the local church.' Spiritual sustenance and support are lessened, and many doctors tend to draw only from colleagues in the hospital, from exam successes and from research projects for the personal satisfaction and fulfillment that they need. As compensation some may seek 'spiritual injections' by attending Christian conferences, but this is incomplete as a solution. As I become more senior in the profession and more involved in committees and clinical work, the more I become convinced that I, along with my family, must be rooted and wholly involved in a live Christian fellowship.

There are, however, some problems here. Some doctors are given special status within a church or Christian fellowship because they are doctors. Special dignity is accorded to their status and they are asked to take on responsibility for which they are not really suited. Academic distinction and leadership qualities within the profession do not necessarily imply that such a person is endowed with special spiritual gifts or discernment. Such involvement may lead to a wrong use of that doctor's time. He may be someone whose time is better spent seizing opportunities for presenting Christian thought and practice within the profession. There is a danger that such a doctor may well be retreating into a secure adulatory environment within the Christian fellowship and as a result live his life in two completely separate compartments. Within the church he lives a ghetto-type existence and within the profession he accepts the prevailing standards and practice.

It may be that is the best we can manage, but surely our dual calling is to be salt and light in society, and also to challenge and stir up our Christian brethren to think through their faith and acquire a truly Christian mind in their work, worship and witness. There are some doctors who give the impression that they are above involvement with ordinary church folk. Perhaps that is rather unkind, but the impression is sometimes given that their medicine demands their special attention and the particular responsibilities of a doctor's work preclude their having any real active involvement in the church fellowship. I have watched with sadness, as over the years, I have seen many such individuals remain churchgoers perhaps, and even be referred to as quiet believers, but they have often seemed to me to be people who have allowed the cares of the profession to enter into their lives so that true spiritual life has been stunted if not choked. My own pastor and I had a slight altercation once. I was rather reluctant about something he wished me to do, and I felt that as a psychiatrist who was professionally involved with some members of the congregation, there were special difficulties in my acceding to this request. His comment was: 'Monty, even a witch doctor has to be a member of the tribe.'

I have seen and heard of so many doctors who have drifted away from Christian things and imperceptibly lost all their commitment. They have ceased from Christian service. The legitimate professional caring for others and their commitment to their career prevents strong links with the Christian fellowship. So they drift, become lukewarm and then cold. It is good to remind ourselves that Our Lord himself needed fellowship and caring within His ministry. It was known who contributed to his keep. It was known to whose home he went for fellowship and a meal. It was known whose garden he visited for times when he specially needed to be alone and to pray.

As Christians we are called to service and to fellowship. There must be time set aside for both. It may be that our significant service is within medicine, contributing a Christian dimension both in thinking and in practice within the profession. But whether this is our service or not, we all need to spend time with other Christians and, as the writer to the Hebrews put it, 'see how each of us may best arouse others to love and active goodness, not staying away from our meetings as some do but rather encouraging one another, all the more because you see the day drawing near'. (Hebrews 10:24 and 25 NEB). Some doctors may use the pressures of time as a way of avoiding such contact with their fellow Christians. However, if our only contact with other Christians is at times of public worship and if we have no regular involvement with others in prayer and Bible study, then I believe we deprive ourselves of what God intends we should have. It is within fellowship that we arouse others and are aroused ourselves to love and good works. Ultimately it is those acts of love and of goodness that will last in God's time, namely eternity.

In the funeral service the Anglican Church there is a marvellous prayer that begins: 'Grant us Lord, the wisdom and the grace to use aright the time that is left to us here on earth…' It is a prayer that every servant of the Lord, be they doctor or not, should pray continually, and although funerals may be times when we pray that with special poignancy, perhaps it should be our daily prayer.

Chapter Ten
AVOIDING BURNOUT

Introduction

May I first give a little personal history. Exactly 60 years ago I was released from hospital having recovered from tuberculous meningitis. I was working as a nursing orderly at a TB hospital when I felt unwell, and was waking with sweats. When I tried to walk, I felt as if at every step my head was being banged by a stick. For one month I was critically ill and expected to die. I spent six months in hospital and was one of the first to have triple therapy, which necessitated daily lumbar punctures for one month. Every so often a new junior doctor would perform this, scraping the nerves and sending shooting pains down my legs. I dreaded hearing the houseman's footsteps on the stairs, knowing what was in store for me.

'Why, O Lord?' I would ask. Abandoned was my ambition to be a missionary in China and yet in due course I realised that this was God's way of pointing me in a different direction. I met my wife and entered the world of psychiatry, partly through the suggestion of a senior physician, Dr Charles Anderson, who had been the first doctor into Belsen when it was liberated in 1945. He asked me one day about my future and whether I had ever thought of specialising in psychiatry, adding the helpful comment, 'You don't have to be bonkers to become a psychiatrist.' I entered the academic unit in Dundee, and when the Professor of Psychiatry was asked to teach a group of theological students and did not want to do it, he asked me to take it on. Thus began my teaching in theological colleges, which

I have now been doing for 50 years in the UK and abroad, and *Burnout* is one of the topics I was often asked about.

Burnout is a term first used in the 1950s in relation to those caring for others. It encompasses tiredness, exhaustion, emotional drain and often depression in those who have given everything for others. The concept has a special application for those in the health professions and in the pastoral ministry who spend their time giving out to those who are needy, whether in body, mind or spirit. Yet there is a sense in which the term produces inherent conflict for Christians. If we don't burn out we may rust out! Should we not aim to burn out in the Lord's work? Or does the Bible encourage us to take care of ourselves, our families and our fellowship?

Take care of yourselves
Many of us, especially in the caring professions, need to be needed, especially by the most needy. It gives us a purpose in our lives and may sometimes be a substitute for other relationships, which helps us to control our own insecurity. We need to have an understanding of ourselves in this respect. We also need to remember that depression is no respecter of persons. We all have our breaking points: they may be different for each of us but they are there for us all. When three 'life events' come together, depression may threaten. That is especially true of 'loss' experiences. These may be bereavements in the family or among close friends or other losses in our lives such as our job or our health or our home, the latter sometimes simply from the trauma of moving to a new area where we have to make new friends.

Acts 20:28 instructs us to 'Keep watch over ourselves.' We need an understanding of who we are. We all have our own personal foibles, though God is able to use us despite our weaknesses. When I was at school my history master gave me a book entitled *Eminent Victorians* by Lytton Strachey. The book is a critique of some nineteenth-century Christian characters and was written to discredit them. But it had the opposite effect on me for I realised that God could use people in a remarkable way in spite of their flaws, and it helped me to look at people as they really are, warts and all, and liberated me from seeing them all as heroes.

Rosemary and I live in Bristol and it was here that George Muller, a teutonic German Christian, devoted his life to caring for orphaned children. John Darby was a fiery Irishman who was the founder of the Exclusive Brethren movement. Both did great things for God but they fell out with each other. One day Darby came to Muller and held out his hand to make up, but Muller responded that there were a few things to discuss first before he would shake Darby's hand. This annoyed Darby, who refused and walked off. They were never reconciled, yet despite their weaknesses and personal animosity God used them both.

We also need to be realistic in our own expectations. Do we have a true vision for the work to which we are called or is it merely a fantasy? Is it a vision given by God that we are able to share and discuss with others, or an unrealistic fantasy of our own making, kept locked in our brain and not brought out, discussed and shared?

We may all have times when we cry out to the Lord as I did with tuberculous meningitis: 'Why, O Lord?' Elisabeth Elliot in her book *Shadow of the Almighty* tells the story of her husband, Jim Elliot, who dedicated himself to missionary work in South America and was killed by the Auca Indians in 1956 while taking the Gospel to that area. In spite of his death it is a triumphal story, fulfilling his words as a 22-year-old: 'He is no fool who gives what he cannot keep to gain what he cannot lose.' Yet Elisabeth Elliot wrote another book, *No Graven Image*, where she describes the death of a patient from anaphylaxis after treatment by a missionary with penicillin. There was no seeming benefit to anyone and she offers no answers as to why this happened. 'Why, O Lord?'

Times of difficulty or ill health can make us pause and take stock and ask 'Where am I going?' Then, often with help from others, we may avoid the temptation to run away or bury our head in the sand and we can stay and work through our situation and find a new path to tread in God's service.

Sometimes we need courage for what seems to be an impossible task that God has asked us to do and then, like Moses, we need to learn that this work is not so much an occupation but rather a commission coming from God. The seeming impossibility of his task was because Moses looked at the job from his point of view, from his limited perspective and not from God's perspective.

Take care of our families

Paul writing to Timothy and Peter in his first letter, speaks of the care we need to take of our families. Communication is important and 'Consider each other' is biblical advice. We need to learn to *listen* to what the other is saying rather than just *hear* what they are saying.

All relationships include extra baggage. Often when teaching about marriage, I would do a stick drawing of a man and wife each with one hand touching but with the other hand behind their back carrying a suitcase. This serves as an illustration of the fact that each brings extra bits and pieces to a relationship, which often need to be unpacked, shared and dealt with.

There are added difficulties in being married to a carer 'called of God'. Children of Christian leaders and missionaries often feel they are in a goldfish bowl, and Marjory Foyle explores this and other causes of stress in Christian workers both married and single in her excellent book, *Honourably Wounded*.

The need for a Sabbath was ordained by God in creation, a day of rest that restores both the individual and the family, and yet Sunday is not a day of rest for many Christian leaders and often not for doctors. The pattern of rest and working is seen throughout God's creation. The heart beats and rests and beats again. We breathe in and we breathe out. Nerve impulses travel down the axons and then there is a recovery period. Muscles cannot contract indefinitely. We sleep, we dream and we wake refreshed. Thus throughout nature there is the pattern of work and rest, and we neglect that at our peril.

We need to learn to protect ourselves and our families. That may mean saying 'no'. On one occasion a lady, a patient of mine, came to church in Bristol with the aim of speaking to me as she knew I would be there. I refused to speak to her about her illness and asked her to come to my consulting rooms on the following Tuesday. She was initially very cross, but she did come on Tuesday and we had a consultation. In due course she started coming more regularly to church, wanting to know about this God that several hundred people came to worship every Sunday, and she became a Christian. Many months later she came up to me again in church but this time she thanked me for refusing to see her on that first Sunday. It had started her on her Christian journey and preserved my sanity.

Take care of the Body of Christ

Romans 12 and Hebrews 10 remind us of the importance of being part of the body of Christ and playing our role in our local church. Ministers and pastors need friends and confidants and should look for support structures both within as well as outside the immediate church setting. There are times when the parson must stop being a parson and become a person.

Paul Berg, while Vicar of Christchurch Clifton in Bristol, had three elderly women in the church who were prayer warriors. John Stott had his Advisory Group of Elders whom he called his 'AGE' group with whom he could discuss which invitations to accept out of the many that came from around the world. Jesus had women as financial supporters, as well as close friends at Bethany where he stayed shortly before his death. Peter, James and John, as well as the other disciples, including Judas, were with him in the upper room, and we need close friends with whom we can share even if we risk being let down as Jesus was.

Even the greatest Christian leaders will have times of grief and trauma and sometimes may become depressed. C S Lewis wrote many books including *The Four Loves*, but in his *A Grief Observed* he describes in very personal terms his grief over the death of his wife. By then he had written books of inestimable help to those going through a time of suffering, none of which were of any help to him in his own deep personal crisis.

There are some questions to which we will never know the answers in this life and some of them may aggravate depression and burnout, but we also need to remember that God is sovereign and he 'works in mysterious ways his wonders to perform'. He gave William Tyndale the ability to translate the Bible into English. Tyndale translated part of it but needed more money to complete the task. The Bishop of London, who objected to his work, told people to buy every copy and burn it. The money raised from the ensuing sales enabled Tyndale to complete the work. The King James version of the Bible drew extensively on Tyndale's translation and within a few years of that publication, a copy was placed in every parish church in England.

Conclusion

As the years pass our abilities will change and not always positively. Teachers may no longer be able to teach, travellers may no longer be able to travel and carers may no longer be able to care. Our health and other life events will overtake us. We are indeed jars of clay. All of us are subject to psychological and physical afflictions. Sometimes we may experience, like Elijah, the 'I and I alone' syndrome, unaware of the others that God has in the background.

Maybe we feel we are on a treadmill and want to say 'stop the world, I want to get off'. The Bible encourages us to consider, reflect, give thought, not forget. As we get older as Christians we will still want to be useful for the Lord but that may be in ways that we have not thought of when we were fitter and more active. Others can help us. Let us foster and use our support structures and let us always remember that God loves us, God is in control and is the Sovereign Lord.

ISSUES IN THE PASTORAL MINISTRY

Chapter Eleven
THE CALL TO MINISTRY AND THE MINISTER'S PERSONAL NEEDS

The call

People enter different careers, professions and jobs for different reasons. We see this in medicine, for example, where the personality of surgeons and psychiatrists is often quite different, and may have influenced their choice of speciality.

So what about the call to the ministry? We rarely talk about ministers' personal needs, but how much do they *need* the kind of work to which they feel God has called them? What does the ministry give them at a personal level? Part of my work as a psychiatrist is to look at these hidden motives and to endeavour to evaluate them.

Freedom and security

On the face of it there is the attraction of release from a humdrum routine. Ministers have no immediate boss. They can suit themselves in many areas and the structure of their day is loose. Yet they also have a certain security (though it may be that security of tenure will soon become a thing of the past). I am aware that the real situation for those in the ministry may well be that they feel they have very little freedom to such an extent that they even feel guilty about taking a day off.

Prestige and respect

Then there is prestige within the community, both in the church community and the wider community where the congregation is situated. There is also for ministers the tangible evidence of total commitment to God that ordination automatically confers. They may not have much money, but within the Christian fellowship they will be respected and their opinion sought after. The ministry therefore provides a sense of being needed and a personal assurance of having found God's will. Does the ministry give ready relationships that are structured, limited and dependent? I suspect that some ministers actually find it very difficult to relate to people easily and naturally in ordinary life. Within any of the caring professions there is a structure to relationships that can be very fulfilling, and at the same time there is also a limit set to them.

Escapism

What about escape from reality? If the prospect of exam failure is looming, the Christian student may begin thinking about the ministry as an easier, more attainable alternative. Older persons in middle life may come across those common feelings of frustration arising from a sense of non-achievement, and may reflect that their profession is not really giving what they expected of their life. The conclusion may be the conviction of a divine call into the ministry.

Don't misunderstand me. I am not saying that God cannot come at such times of crisis and lay hold of certain people to lead them into the ministry. What I am saying is that we need to be alert to possible motives, which may be very different from a true call to serve God, and we may all too easily mistake certain inner feelings for his call.

Atonement for the past

How much is the call to the ministry part of some people's conversion? The new birth produces a dedication to God, which can be confused with a call to be a minister. It may even be that after conversion there is a desire to make some atonement for the manner of life in which one formerly lived. I offer you an example of what I mean. Charles Kingsley, the author of *The Water Babies*, was a sensitive man who was able to write in a perceptive way. He wrote to his fiancée: 'Day after day there has been an involuntary still small voice directing me to the church as the only rest for my troubled spirit in this world. I did not know the reason for this strange haunting of the mind though I thought it was the only atonement I could make in the eyes of the world for my offences. I feel, Fanny, that I am under a heavy debt to God. How can I pay this better than by devoting myself to the religion I have scorned? Making of a debaucher a preacher of purity and holiness and of the destroyer of systems, a weak though determined upholder of the only true system.' The comment was made, 'He sealed his return to faith with a vow to become a clergyman.' His fiancée was also caught up in the vow. Although she went along with it, it was not a particularly good situation and there were unhappy consequences. However, in those days there were very few options open to someone of her class and position if the husband or fiancé decided to follow a certain course or profession. It seems that Kingsley's choice of the ministry was his atonement for his past rather than a choice he and Fanny considered fully together before God.

Hidden motivations

There are many people who speak about their call who are not able to reflect and communicate in the way Kingsley did. The more subjective, the more inward, personal and associated with other life events the call is, the more vulnerable ministers will be to stress and difficulty later on in their ministries. The more hidden the motivations, the more likely they are to be caught out by those motivations if and when they are unfulfilled.

Personal reflection

God may indeed be calling, and someone may sense and recognise that call. But ministers also need to ask themselves what personal and psychological investments are involved. No one should be afraid or ashamed to look at their motives throughout their ministry. After all we try to train our children to reflect on their behaviour and the way we discipline them. God has called to the ministry, but in the same way it is helpful to those he has called to think carefully what other aspects there are in that call that may be confusing and contaminating. Ministers need to reflect on these things. They may need to smile wryly and make a few adjustments.

Fulfilment

Jean Coggan's book, *Wife to the Archbishop*, illustrates this well. When she became engaged to Donald he was a curate in Islington. Here Donald Coggan was called to preach the Word to the poor and underprivileged. Jean was fascinated by it all, for here in Islington people were in need. It was a parish of 19,000 reflecting the poverty of the Great Depression. Here at last she felt there might be a real work for her to do among the teeming crowds her husband longed to serve. An immensely loyal woman, and a tremendous support to her husband, she found herself fulfilled in ministering to the needs of the people in the parish.

They then moved to Canada when her husband became Principal of the Toronto College of Divinity. It was there that Jean suddenly became aware of an unexpected and insidious feeling that all was not well with her. A darkness of spirit entirely alien to her hopeful nature had begun to engulf her. She had nothing to do. Deep in her heart she wanted people, she wanted to be needed. Now she felt useless for she apparently had no role to play. The only 'useful' thing she did was to be a sort of college taxi-driver. She commented, 'I can't find God. I have no sense of reality. I feel completely blank towards God.' She came through that time, but she discovered that something that she had previously seen as an essential part of her call had now gone. From her description, it seems to me that her call to spiritual ministry had become entangled with her personal needs.

Sociological considerations

Financial stringency

Another issue that faces many clergy regarding their call is financial stringency. I was recently reading through the medical notes of a minister's child when I was astonished and disturbed to see the person classified by an outside professional observer as 'Social Status: Low Income Family'. Those words had a starkness that shook me. Yet hospitality is expected of the minister's family. Ministers with private, independent means are a thing of the past. It is often a struggle for vicarage families to make ends meet, especially for wives who choose not to pursue paid employment.

Middle-class culture
Ministers are also faced with the tension between Christian and middle-class culture. Sometimes they are first-generation believers with no Christian background. This creates difficulties in two areas of ministry: first, ministers from such a background will have no Christian models from their home, and maybe not from their wider families and relationships. Second, they have the uncertainty of sorting out what are truly Christian attitudes from what are merely middle-class attitudes. When I was a student we were motivated by words like 'sacrifice', 'discipline' and 'Christian austerity'. The new generation of Christians smile at such concepts. There is a real tension as values one generation considered essential for every Christian are now questioned and even rejected.

Mobility
In addition, there is the problem of mobility and the call to move from one parish to another. Our society is affected by a sense of loosened roots, and this affects ministers as well. Some advocate a shorter spell in a parish, but what are the effects of frequent moves on wives and families? Equally important, though too often ignored, church members are subjected to the repeated loss of their pastors, with a traumatic bereavement experience each time. Some pastors see that as good for the parish, but there are other ways of looking at it. As fellowships become transient and less stable and their pastors slip through after short ministries, an increasing burden falls on those church members who are fixed and permanent. Such people are then less able to keep supporting their ministers' families in the way they should and would like to do.

Perhaps it may seem, particularly to those reading this who are about to start in the ministry, that I am bringing into question the whole concept of the call. Not at all. That is between you and God on the one hand and the people who train and commission you on the other. My point is that alongside the very real, spiritual aspects of the call of God, other aspects of our God-given humanity are also involved. Those called to the ministry need also to take account of their personal and emotional needs, and not think about the ministry only in terms of spiritual needs. After all, we are fallen men and women and have all the afflictions entailed in the Fall. Those afflictions include the clouding of our motives. If we do not recognise these implications of our fallenness, when times of severe stress overtake us, such issues may confound us and cause us to doubt or question our call. Mercifully God is much more gracious with us than we are with ourselves.

Chapter Twelve
THE MINISTER'S EXPECTATIONS OF THEIR MINISTRY, THEIR BACKGROUND AND PERSONALITY

Expectations of ministry

I often ask ministers, 'What expectations did you have of your ministry when you set out to train? What are your expectations now of how the Lord will work through you? What do you consider your forte? Do you have a secret daydream? Have you a personal ambition, even fantasy, that niggles away somewhere in the back of your mind, something nobody knows about, least of all the person who knows you best? Something you may have only told yourself and you hardly admit to God that you have such a dream.'

These expectations need to come out into the open, certainly before God and also before some other trusted friend. These fantasies often give a clue to that part of our motivation where failure to achieve makes us most vulnerable. Often we are not honest with ourselves. We deny these expectations, but we still daydream about them from time to time.

Frustrated ambitions

Some hope to be specialists with young people but then find they lose their rapport as they grow older. Others hope to be great preachers but never have a church that gives them the needed scope. Yet others see themselves as competent counsellors, modern reformed pastors like Richard Baxter, spending fruitful time with people to help them. But they find that their parishioners bare their souls, not to their minister, but to their GP or their social worker. Did you once dream of a famous pulpit? Of many conversions? Of a parish in renewal? Or were you going to be a great church planter? Yet God may have called you, not to greatness in human eyes, but to obscurity instead. You may have even become someone who closes down churches or amalgamates them rather than plants them! Remember that the Apostle John was arguably the greatest pastor in the New Testament. His writings convey an enormously sensitive pastoral heart but God allowed him to be sent away from his beloved people to the little island of Patmos.

The example of Elijah
We can learn from Elijah. There was no doubt about God's call to this man or his enabling of him. Yet after the triumph on Mount Carmel he became profoundly depressed. 'I have had enough Lord, take away my life... I am no better than my ancestors ...I have been very zealous for the Lord ... I am the only one left and now they are trying to kill me too.'

God's first approach was to supply him with food, drink, rest and sleep, the very same physical treatments for depression we would use today. But then God took Elijah off to Mount Sinai for some psychotherapy and Elijah started talking and the underlying issues spilled out. He had come to rely on the spectacular and after a truly amazing demonstration on Carmel of rugged faith in God, he now slides into the snare of trusting in himself, not God. Earlier on he had had many miracles to give spectacular confirmation that God was really with him. But now the miracles were no longer coming and Jezebel was threatening his life. Feeling let down and forsaken by God, he fled. Is there also in his complaint that he is no better than the prophets before him, a hint of a secret desire to excel and outdo others in his service for God? Perhaps there was a competitive streak in Elijah, a secret passion to serve God more effectively than others had done. Previously, full of his own importance, Elijah had given little credence to the weak-kneed Obadiah who may have seemed to have compromised to keep his nose clean at Ahab's court (Elijah would appear to have no idea of what Obadiah had achieved as a servant of God in a high, civic position). He, Elijah,

116

was the only man after God's heart. He confronted Ahab. He tackled the prophets of Baal single-handedly at Carmel while all the rest dithered or remained in hiding.

Then the miracles stopped and his expectation of the spectacular was shattered. It was then the power of Jezebel came home to him, and like Peter suddenly noticing the wind and waves, he took his eyes off God and forgot all that God had done for and through him. In his zeal and subsequent 'low' he had distorted the facts. He had a plan in his mind of how things should happen based on his past experience and his daydreams of personal importance. When it did not work out that way, he amended the facts so that he could wallow in his self-pity more effectively. He felt that God had let him down. His expectations had not been fulfilled in quite the way he had wanted. God had to use Elisha and two pagan kings to continue the work, as we read in 1 Kings 19:15-17. Elijah's public ministry appears to have finished.

How often I have seen this pattern in God's servants who have perhaps taken a wrong course or not fulfilled their own expectations, but we do not read about them. Biographies are not written about failures, about those who do not fit into our stereotypes of success in the ministry, however much God may have been using them.

A fruitful 'failure'

William Chalmers Burns was one such 'failure' who is scarcely known today, although in my opinion his work and influence merit an up-to-date assessment. He was a Scot who gave up his career as a lawyer to train for the ministry in the 1830s. His father was a faithful and godly Church of Scotland minister who had preached in Kilsyth for 40 years and seen little fruit. Then one sermon preached by William in 1839 brought dramatic revival. Hundreds of people were permanently changed in the following weeks. Notorious drunkards became sober, wife batterers started caring for their wives and families. The whole community was transformed. The local presbytery was so astonished that they set up a commission to investigate. The commission reported, 'We have looked at this...and find that truly the work is standing.' It was a remarkable work of God that profoundly affected that community for decades thereafter. Later, Burns preached for a few months in St Peter's Dundee, the church of Robert Murray McCheyne, the most celebrated preacher in Scotland at that time, who had seen much blessing during his seven years there. In McCheyne's absence, another revival broke out during Burns' ministry there, which within a few months spread throughout Scotland and profoundly affected the Church there for the next 50 years.

During these short spells, William Burns reaped where others had sown. However, he became convinced he should obey his original call to China and there he served faithfully for 20 years. But he saw very few converts and it was only after his death that others reaped where he had laboured, vibrant churches being established in each centre where he had worked. Furthermore, he deeply influenced others who worked in inland China and was frequently consulted by Hudson Taylor over the founding of the China Inland Mission. Hudson Taylor said of Burns after his death, 'He was the holiest man I ever knew.' It was Burns who introduced Taylor to the interior of China and showed him how to live as a Chinese instead of as a westerner in China. This now forgotten man was ultimately one of the most influential of all the pioneers to China, one of God's great men. But in the eyes of the world his ministry in China was a failure, a mistake and a waste of great gifts.

God's secret purposes

God may have very different ideas for us from those with which we started out. Woe betide us if we carry our daydreams and fantasies around with us like Elijah. God may not only give us no apparent blessing but also may even ask us to close down a work. General Booth is reported to have said, 'God can often find men to start up a work; it is not so easy to find a man who will stop it when His need for it has ceased.' Many ministers, missionaries and church members are too attached to their work. They are vulnerable to depression should they become redundant in a spiritual or secular context. There is a difference between a daydream and a vision. The minister who has their own idea of what God is calling them to do must beware. Disillusionment lies in the way of daydreams and personal expectations. Vision must always be open to scrutiny and should be shared with others for their criticism and encouragement. We need that sober assessment all the time.

Ministers' background and personality

We turn now to consider the impact on the ministry of a minister's family background and personality, the family being the laboratory of human relationships and functions that God has ordained for us.

Personality problems

It is all too easy to stereotype the expectations of a minister's behaviour and to set up a prototype of the ideal minister or minister's spouse. The problem is that nobody will fit that mould. We all have aspects within our personalities that some may denigrate and quirks that we may hold on to as a matter of principle.

Let me illustrate the kind of problem I have in mind. An early experience of bereavement is known to make people more prone to depression later in life. Such an early bereavement will prime the way we look at life, so that we may be less able to withstand the stresses that come from loss and change. This priming will probably be present all our lives. Although God's grace can come into that area, it remains as a fact of our lives and facts can cause problems. In the same way, it is known that the absence of a parent of the same sex, or an appropriate substitute during puberty can be associated with sexual and relationship problems in later life. Clergy families are no more immune to such problems than any other families, but they may find it very difficult to come to terms with them. They may think that they should not be feeling like this, since they assume God ought to be changing the problem area. I am not denying that God does work in our lives to produce in us more of the fruits of grace. However, it is foolish to deny that our genes, our culture and our habit formations do affect our personalities. They affect the way we relate to one another. That must include our marriage partners and those we work with in our parishes. They also affect the pattern of our ministries.

Men and women with strong passions
Take the Apostle Paul. There is an aggressive, thrusting aspect to his personality and his relationship with colleagues. There is a contentiousness in his personal allusions. Look at his disagreements with Peter, John Mark and Barnabas. On the other hand, he had the strength and independence necessary for a pioneer apostle, freed from the ties of family. I wonder how Timothy regarded him and whether he was affected by the sheer force of Paul's personality?

Or consider John Wesley. He was strongly attached to his forceful mother, a mother who governed her numerous children by the bell and taught them to cry silently. He derived much of his drive, discipline and tendency to over-organise from her. There is no doubt that his father was an ineffective man, that John had a rather special relationship with his mother and that he never coped well with women at a pastoral level. He was frequently getting into scrapes and had to leave America because of difficulties there. His relationships with women were complex, and his own marriage was an extremely unhappy one. His wife was a very difficult woman but he was an insensitive, neglectful and very ambivalent husband, the sort of man who would have driven most wives spare. By contrast, Charles Wesley was completely uxorious. Besotted with his wife and family, he needed a good nudge from John now and then to get him back to work.

George Burton, formerly of the Mayflower Centre, is another example of a man shaped by his past experience for a God-given role. Brought up in the grinding poverty of the slums of Glasgow, his life pattern was one of indiscipline, indulgence and violence. Yet despite his very difficult personality and nearly psychopathic relationships, following his conversion he was able to reach the unbelieving working classes of East London in a unique way. However, he found it immensely difficult to get on with his fellow workers at the Mayflower Centre and because of his background he left many scars on those to whom he reacted in an aggressive way, especially those whom he saw as his social superiors. Indeed, his biography was also an exorcism of the abrasive impact that he left on his co-workers.

Sober self-assessment

We need to see how this applies to our own lives in general and to the lives of ministers in particular. The danger is that these aspects and facets of our behaviour may not be recognised. Wrong diagnosis leads us into practical difficulties. Ministers may come to blame others for problems that are inherent in themselves. Not realising their own personality traits, they may think that it is the Gospel that is being rejected when they find themselves at loggerheads with their congregations and elders. What may have started out as a hidden personality clash becomes elevated to a defence of principle, and the more theological that principle is, the more rigid, righteous and entrenched their position becomes. So it is important for ministers to recognise their foibles and take proper account of them, otherwise these foibles may catch them out. But if we can recognise our problems then we have the opportunity to become more truly humble, more open to change, more able to accept help and more sensitive to the problems of others. In the same way, part of the training of psychiatrists is to help them deal with their own personalities and backgrounds and recognise ways these could hinder them from helping and treating patients.

We need to acquire that 'sober assessment' of ourselves of which Paul speaks in Romans 12:3. If we can acquire a real, down-to-earth self-assessment, then it is possible for us to grow. We can become more sensitive to others and more truly humble and reachable ourselves. We can change, we can mature. In this way we will add to our personal resources and be better able to cope with crises in our lives and ministry. Surely this is what the doctrine of regeneration is about. We all have our old family traumas, our faulty pattern of training, our flawed inheritance. But we do not have to cling to these old models of behaviour or to act out old instinctive drives. We have a new law, a new model, a new power, as Paul writes in Philippians 3:12: 'not that we are already perfect, but we press on for the upward call of God in Christ Jesus'.

Chapter Thirteen
THE MINISTER AND THE FELLOWSHIP

In theological colleges and manuals of pastoralia, much is taught about the minister's devotional and prayer life and relationship with God. One book by Owen Branden of St. Augustine's College at Canterbury, *The Pastor and his Ministry*, speaks of the minister as a servant, teacher, guide, theologian and priest. He writes nothing about the pastor as a member of the fellowship, a member of the body. Nor does he write about the pastoral needs of ministers themselves or who should pastor the pastors.

Help for the helpers
In the secular world, there is a great deal of talk about help for the helpers. Especially in psychiatry, there is an awareness that those who are giving out emotionally and are involved with people in support and counselling, are themselves in need of support and care. The secular world, therefore, has set up support structures with management courses, special training courses, group leaders' courses, encounter groups, psychotherapy supervision, or personal therapy. The medical world has its clinical teams, with shared responsibility for the patients. For ministers the availability of pastoral support varies greatly.

How then does the minister receive support?
I will outline two patterns of ministry that I have observed. My aim is to use these rather caricatured cardboard cut-outs to focus on the underlying attitudes of many ministers, and the effect this has on the personal care and support they give and receive.

The minister as leader of the fellowship

This type of minister may be found leading any sort of church or para-church society. Those who fulfil this kind of role would have done well in business as executives. Their churches are highly efficient, with a splendid hierarchy of committees and an endless flow of information. Such ministers professionalise their work and become detached from the fellowship. They become preoccupied with techniques of counselling, house visiting, church growth or evangelism. The result can be most impressive, with well-run churches ticking over very well. This is often the pattern of the successful, middle-class parish in a university town. There is superb music, excellent preaching and high-calibre assistants or curates. The ministers see real numerical growth, and are very fulfilled by a sense of God working through them. However, the church cannot but be dependent on the individual pastor and the glory begins to depart once the minister moves on. We have many vast ecclesiastical shells that are memorials to particular ministers, or to a succession of good ministerial 'managing directors'.

In themselves, these situations are not wrong. Indeed, they have a special role within a city or diocese, for setting standards, training and reaching out. These large and efficient churches are a real source of stimulus and encouragement to more struggling fellowships. But they also can have real problems. The great snare is that when these fellowships become clerically dependent, they never grow in depth and maturity. The members are not able to exercise fully their own gifts as the ministers themselves are so gifted. The congregations become passive recipients rather than active participants and so cannot mature. At worst, this pattern of ministry can give rise to clerical *prima donnas*, who lord it over God's heritage and the congregation becomes a flowing tide of commuters and passengers.

This is still seen today in certain evangelical circles. Some ministers are always fussing over their members, counselling them, combing their hair and straightening their ties, so to speak. They cannot take their hands off and allow them to experience a little bit of pain. They are people who have a great *need* to care and that can be a dangerous quality. Their products are dependent on them, little marching saints who will do exactly as expected, going out into the world with their tight programmes and manuals of techniques. This may be helpful for some in the early days of their Christian life, but does not produce maturity. Such fussing and overdisciplining never allows people to grow and take responsibility.

The effects on the minister

If these are some of the possible effects on the fellowship of such a ministry, what are the effects on the minister's personal life? The spouses of such ministers are frequently depressed unless they acquire careers of their own and lead semi-independent lives. They thought they had married a minister, not a tycoon. Now they find themselves with all the problems of a tycoon's partner, but without the money or the parties! In the previous parish, the wife might have been very fulfilled, running the Sunday School, leading the women's organisation, opening the fete, but now there are powerful people around, well able to do those tasks. The ministers themselves may run into grave difficulties when their drive goes, their enthusiasm wanes, their health deteriorates or personal problems arise; they have never been close enough to anyone to ask for help. They get the Elijah complex. If they are fortunate, the ministry department or bishop finds a little field somewhere to put the poor soul out to pasture.

Not a biblical pattern

I want to suggest this is not a biblical pattern of ministry. These ministers' support (such as it is) largely comes from fellow clergy, who are of course separate from the fellowship. They rely on the professionalism of the ministry, with its skills, resources and experience. No personal support comes from the staff meetings, which are run like business board meetings, with the rector or minister as an aloof boss. This is a secular pattern, closely analogous to the medical consultant with his junior staff. The staff meeting becomes like a ward round: I am the boss as the consultant, but want to hear what my staff have to say. Let us not despise these churches; but the more ministers tend towards such an attitude, the more impoverished all become. The fellowship is deprived of the minister's personal contribution, and the minister is deprived of the fellowship's support. This is also a great source of minister–assistant vicar–curate tension, because the minister or vicar does not relate to anyone in the fellowship, including the assistant or curate.

Clerical professionalism
Some forms of the modern team ministries can be like this, in that they emphasise this clerical professionalism. They can become very analogous to the medical group practices at health centres: a different doctor on call each night and a deputy at weekends. But when your gut is sore at midnight, you want your own doctor. The group practice may be an efficient and logical system, but it has major defects. There is no sense of belonging, no opportunity for caring or deeper healing, and there is no involvement or consistent feedback to the doctor in the medical field or to the clergyman within the parish. Something is lost that is of the essence of pastoring the flock and being part of the fellowship.

The minister as servant of the fellowship
Here is a much more person-oriented minister. Those who are 'servants' are much less concerned with organisation and preaching, and far more involved in visiting, counselling and caring. They allow greater flexibility, are more available as persons and are loved by their people. Often they will have a profound influence on the fellowship, though they can be the despair of their family and assistant ministers or curates. They have time for everyone and everything; they allow the home to be invaded, meals to go cold and family outings to be cancelled. They neglect their own needs and the needs of their families.

They may also neglect the need to discipline those clamouring for their aid. They may bring problem people into the home, psychiatric patients and people with disturbed personalities, and set up a system of communal living. Often the result is increased distress within the family, depression in the spouse, and sometimes disillusionment in the minister. A number of prominent clergy have recently spoken openly about depression in their spouses and families, as their home was invaded by all this caring. This has been written about by Floyd McClung in his book about the Dilorum family, a group of young people involved with hippies in Kabul, in their book *Just off Chicken Street*: 'The need for privacy can become a serious problem. I was guilty of being too preoccupied by the needs of the Dilorum family and not mindful enough of my wife's right to unshared private life. We needed more time alone, more time to share; just the two of us.'

Now to some extent, all ministers experience that tension. But as with the first example, the minister who serves in this way produces a clerically dependent fellowship, with people who never grow and mature. They are used to everything being done for them and have an expectation of instant availability, with inordinate time being spent on their problems. They have never been allowed to feel the pain of taking responsibility, of facing confrontation, or of limits being set on what is offered. Thus they cannot learn more mature ways of behaving. Children need love, the setting of limits and the imposing of discipline in order to grow up and mature; the same is true of members of the fellowship.

An attempted solution
Arising out of these tensions in seeking to be a servant, many ministers seek some expertise to help them discern a person's central problem more easily. The special skill acquired helps the minister to handle the situation better, while also protecting himself or herself. In the United States, this is seen to an extreme degree, where the theological student has to undergo personal psychotherapy, and many ministers get into pastoral counselling.

The dangers of such training in 'pastoral counselling' have been well outlined by a Jesuit, Père André Godin: 'Books devoted to the study of personality, or an elementary psychiatry for the clergy, can accustom him to substituting a system of labels and classification for the complex task of the true mental discernment and moral support. At first, this facility seems tempting, but in the end it spoils contact with the real person by removing him and placing him behind the bars of a conceptual scheme. A genuine pastoral psychology must be especially severe with these pseudo-psychological works, from which the reader is supposed to learn the art of making converts, winning vocations, and commanding an audience. Appealing to the urge for power and promising to yield the secret of influencing people, without having to learn how to be open to others, such books are nothing but a caricature of psychological work in general and of pastoral work in particular.'

Much the same can be said of Western countries, where many ministers set great store by their specialist ministries; the snare is that there is an associated professionalism, the professionalism of the counsellor, the healer, the therapist, or the church growth expert. They may acquire considerable expertise, at some cost; but in addition to distancing themselves from their fellowship, they also very rarely acquire recognition from the professionals among whom they work. The minister sees himself as a professional, but is rarely accepted by other professionals, resulting in immense frustration.

Frustration and isolation

A particular example of the frustration and isolation of the specialist minister is often seen in the hospital chaplain. He is part of the staff, but not part of the clinical team: he has no access to the clinical records or the ward rounds and there may even be hostility from the medics. Some years ago I spoke to a group of hospital chaplains. They exploded with frustration that they could at last let loose, with a real doctor in front of them. There was nothing personal about their outburst; they were expressing their pent-up frustration that came out of their unfulfilled aspirations.

A book by Frank Wright on the pastoral ministry puts this well: 'Even in hospitals and prisons, where chaplains have a well-defined pastoral role, pastors sometimes feel as if they are optional extras: tolerated, but not significant. There is a loneliness arising from their profession as pastor, in addition to the inescapable loneliness of the human condition.' So what is the personal support of ministers in these specialised areas? So often it is other clergy, supplemented by the need and gratitude of those seeking aid. The minister becomes greedy for situations of need, and hangs on to them because they are sustaining him in a particular way.

A more biblical model

Ministers who adopt either of these approaches, *leading* or *serving*, may well be left isolated. They are outside the fellowship of which they are members. The result may be that those who are pastors have no pastor themselves. So from where should ministers and their families receive support and sustaining? Surely it is from the body of Christ, of which they are parts; from the fellowship to which they are ministering. We shall go on to look in some depth at a biblical model in which ministers are members of the fellowship.

The minister as a member of the fellowship

When patients see me in my clinic, or are admitted to my ward in hospital, they have been sent to me because they are sick; I treat them, and the state of my health is irrelevant. Similarly, those who go to a counsellor have problems to sort out; a contract is made, and it is considered irrelevant whether the counsellor has problems within himself or herself or not. In both cases, the relationship must be strictly professional. However, the same is not true when someone within the fellowship comes to the minister; the member has needs and so does the minister. Furthermore, they belong to each other as brothers and sisters in Christ. It is the failure both to see and experience this, which lies behind some of the most distressing situations that I have had to deal with in Christian workers' lives and families.

No pastor

Many ministers refuse to have a pastor, and many cannot find one when they need it. Like doctors, ministers are supposed to be able to look after themselves, they are professional carers, so surely (the question goes) they do not need anyone to care for them, do they? When I discussed this with a very able and godly French minister, and asked him who his pastor was, he just shrugged his shoulders and replied, 'The Lord'.

The essential cause of this is that since entering theological college, ministers' supporters are largely clerical. Their sustenance has been the company of other clergy, with fraternals, retreats and conferences. How inadequate they prove; they are the very worst places for ministers to be pastored! Ministers meet and discuss their work, with banal generalities about recent encouragements. I myself have spoken at ministers' fraternals and seen how little real sharing goes on. How can you say you are depressed and feel a failure, that the work is going badly and you feel responsible? How can you share that your home life is in chaos, with your wife having gone off you sexually, and the children acting up mercilessly? All you can share is vague generalities, and exaggerate the spiritual growth of the work.

Clergy do not care well for other clergy, doctors care very badly for other doctors and lawyers give terrible advice to fellow lawyers because in each case they identify too closely with the other person. In medicine, we are well aware of this, if a little ashamed of ourselves. When I see a doctor as one of my patients, I have to remind myself that while in my clinic, he is just someone who has problems. I may meet him later in committees, and see many issues in him that I recognise in myself; yet I must regard him as a person who is depressed. I know that my heart is beating faster and my blood pressure rising, but if I make concessions simply because he is a doctor, I will eventually run into trouble. Some doctors find this easier than others; but we do not care well for our kith and kin because we identify in this way. Now, theoretically, episcopal churches should give better pastoral care to their minister. I have been immensely impressed with the caring of some bishops. But I do know that not every bishop gives this sort of support. Nor have I found the quasi-bishops and fellow ministers of the reformed churches particularly good at giving support either. When a crisis blows up, the pastoral machinery sometimes works well; but it rarely prevents a crisis. The real question is how to deal with issues before the crisis blows up.

A shocking story

Some time ago as the consultant on call for that day, I was asked to see a minister who had become profoundly depressed. It was the beginning of an ongoing saga, from which I am quoting with his express permission. Having become depressed, he wrote the following letter to the person who should have had pastoral care of him:

The position here is becoming increasingly impossible; the problems are worsening each week, the pressure is steadily mounting in me to do something. In this tense situation, some action must be taken; the only real answer is to bring my ministry to a close. You will appreciate that this has not been decided lightly or without regret. The last two years here have been dark indeed, testing my faith to its uttermost depths. I cannot yet say that light shines but only that faith beckons towards that which might be light. In the circumstances, I do not ask for more than that, although I am sure that eventually light will dawn. The implications of this step are far reaching, and I would appreciate your advice and comments on the necessary procedures to be taken regarding church, house, etc.

The pastoral reply came back:

Thank you for your letter of the 21st. I am sorry that you feel you must leave the ministry. Nevertheless, if this action helps you to clarify your own mind, and to open for you a field in which you can successfully serve, then I wish you well on the course on

which you are about to embark. Now I came to practical matters. I presume you have obtained a local authority grant, to keep you and your family during your proposed course of study. You ask for my comments and advice about church and house: it seems to me that having now made up your mind to take this course, you should resign as from three months time. You cannot reasonably expect the church and the other churches in the area which have been wanting to have a group ministry for some time to wait indefinitely. As the house will be required for the leader of the new group, you should apply to the local authority for housing. As you are aware, you occupy the house on a service tenancy.
Kind regard s to yourself and your wife.

This was a most harrowing experience. That minister had an expectation of support and sustaining during the worst crisis of his life. I am very glad to say that some clergy from another denomination gave him and his family the spiritual support they needed during that time. It was I who had to minister to him when he ground to a halt. To add insult to injury, after a long period of no formal connection with his denomination, he received from one of the church's committees a letter sent five years to the day after he had resigned his charge. It was a formal duplicated letter, which read:

We have been asked to review the list of clergy not in pastoral charge; the chairman has asked if any member knew of the following ... (there followed a list of names, among which was his own). That was the ongoing pastoral support he received!

Fantasy fellowships
What lies at the root of such situations? Though I have taught in theological colleges for many years, and believe that they have a very real place in training, in my view they have much to answer for here. So often, ministers never learn to relate to a fellowship after leaving college.

The Anglican college of Cuddesdon, outside Oxford, was started by 'Soapy Sam' Wilberforce when his curates and ordinands began to share life together in his house. When he then institutionalised it, a great opportunity was lost; something which was of the essence of what he gave in the early days was gone. A college has an *esprit de corps*, a fantasy fellowship, which becomes the ideal. The minister's craving for that former fantasy fellowship is insatiable. The church fellowship that now seeks to embrace the minister is somehow inadequate. Is the reason for this that seeds of clericalism are sown in the college days, as an expectation of fellowship largely with fellow clergy develops? I am caricaturing, but it seems to me that this inadequacy is present in, and stems from, most colleges.

Spouse's resentment

If the student is married, college may mark the beginning of the spouse's resentment, especially if they have a family. The spouse may feel excluded from the college fellowship: the breakfast, the worship and the lecture. She cannot be involved with him in the local church fellowship either; and often feels that she goes down spiritually while he feels that he is expanding, maturing and gaining much from college life. This clericalism develops into isolationism, and non-communication with the congregation. How congregations smart under the verbal lashings of new curates! Charles Simeon called them 'congregation butchers'. He had been one himself once.

Shared responsibility

I well remember being surprised and challenged when my minister first shared his difficulties with me. That stimulated prayer, concern and commitment on my part. There must be persons within each church, some family perhaps, with whom ministers can pray and talk, expressing their fears, doubts and difficulties. There must be those who will 'own' their ministers, loving them, binding up their wounds, comforting them and even helping them financially. Our problem is that we are so often exclusive that this becomes destructive when it should lead to a sharing of responsibility, when the minister shares things with a few confidants in the fellowship. Despite that, some colleges still teach against having close friends within the congregation.

Daring vulnerability

'God trusted himself to a carpenter and his wife', Harry Williams has written. 'Christ trusted himself to Judas and to Peter.' That is vulnerability!

Things are changing and a new generation of ordinands are much more aware of the issues, though they may well get a tough time at college because of this new attitude. Why cannot a student and family be truly linked to a local fellowship and freed from the tug of loyalties? They could become involved in the local church, not with the ordinand as an extra assistant, but the whole family as ordinary Christians taking an active part in that church, as members of the fellowship. That would help the student to listen, to learn and to be ministered to by the fellowship. Many of the leading laypersons, from whom most is expected, need the clergy to understand their many pressures, not thrash them to ever deeper commitment. The minister feels he cannot share with his assistant, as the assistant is only there temporarily to be trained. The assistant feels he cannot share with the supervisor who is the assistant's boss and will be writing reports and references. Many congregations have no concept of care. But equally, there are many men and women within those congregations who are able to care, but afraid to offer. The first move may have to come from the minister. God will call us to account for our failure to minister to our ministers, and will call ministers to account for their failure to allow the fellowship to minister to them.

The Lord's carers

Jesus had his favourites. It was well known who his special friends were. It was known which house gave him a particular welcome and some good food. It was known which women supported him. Surely it is within the fellowship that our true supports must be. It is within the fellowship that all Christians have something of themselves invested in each other, as we bear one another's burdens. It is within the fellowship that our minds, even our minister's mind, is renewed. Here the ministers can receive feedback on their ministries and a sober appraisal of themselves. Here the spouse and family can belong, and the difficult adolescent children of the pastoral family can find other adults to relate to and identify with. I know that these are words of perfection; congregations are not always like that. But the fellowship will never be like this unless the ministers preach it, look for it, pray for it and then pioneer it themselves. Unless they are prepared to be open and vulnerable, how will congregations be prepared to open up to them?

Investments

If ministers function as professionals within their fellowships, they will be treated and used as professionals. Clients do not want to know about the needs or difficulties of their professional carer. The body has only one head and in terms of the church that is Christ. For the fellowship to mature, it needs to become truly the body of Christ and ministers must become a part of the body. Christ is the head, not the minister. They tell their congregations that they are a fellowship, a *koinonia*, with shares invested in each other. What shares do the ministers have invested in their fellowship? Do they enter into fellowship with them, sharing their weaknesses and also their visions?

Support

I am sometimes asked, not as a psychiatrist, but as an ordinary Christian person, to assess missionary candidates and future ministers. As well as looking at family and marital relationships, I look at who is sending and supporting them. If they have not received care themselves, then I question who is calling them to care for others.

A Scottish divine has expressed this well: 'The point is that none of us can work effectively on our own. We must be sent out by the church, by the praying church, whatever nondescript company of Christians that might be... many missionaries feel out on a limb, and all on their own. They may well question their calling unless they can find help and guidance to relate themselves to some group somewhere who are prepared to own them, and who will care for them.' Ministers serving in hard situations face similar pressures. Many of those I know who have gone into situations that were regarded as hopeless have again and again found a couple of old saints to share with, pray with and who have taken a special care for them as a family where previously they had viewed the situation as devoid of that kind of support! Two or three will do who are willing to own, care for and thrust their minister forth into battle. Ministers may not discover this until they have their first charge and then they discover that, all unknown to them, certain people had been patiently fishing in all the waters for their new minister, until up he came and both 'fish' and 'fisher' met with delight. Alas, if ministers do not want or expect such people, they will not find them!

Full integration

Michael Griffiths, in his excellent book *Cinderella with Amnesia*, writes: 'I seriously wonder whether a high percentage of problems about which Christians seek counselling would ever arise at all, if they had been properly instructed congregationally, and fully integrated into the fellowship of God's people.' I am sure that is true, and that it is truest when ministers themselves are part of such fellowships.

After lecturing one day in a theological college, a perplexed-looking student came up to me and asked, 'If I had someone like you in my congregation, what would you expect of me?' I was stumped as I had never been asked that before nor thought in those terms. My reply was: 'I would hope you would study and expound the Word, helping me to apply it to every aspect of my life so that I was not living in two worlds.' Now, reviewing my experience of the great needs of ministers, I would add, 'You need to be one with us and in order to do that, we both need to be members of the fellowship.' Who is sufficient for these things? It is God who enables us, and a living fellowship is part of that enabling.

Issues in Cross-Cultural Mission

Chapter Fourteen
MISSION AS POLYHABITING PLURAL WORLDS: INSIGHTS FROM THE LIFE AND MISSION OF MONTAGU BARKER
Brainerd Prince

Introduction

O ne of the first memories I have of Dr Barker, as his students called him in Union Biblical Seminary before he became 'Uncle' to many of us, is that of sitting in his class on *Pastoral Care and Counselling* listening to his lecture on different kinds of mental illness. Even as he spoke I began to get a strange feeling that he was talking about me. He went on to say: 'Schizophrenia is a brain disorder that affects the way a person behaves, thinks and sees the world. People with schizophrenia often have an altered perception of reality. They may see or hear things that don't exist, speak in strange or confusing ways, believe that others are trying to harm them, or feel like they're being constantly watched.' I was completely convinced that I had schizophrenia and raised my hand in class. I told him with utmost seriousness, even as the whole class laughed, that I felt I had experienced the symptoms that he had just described. He didn't laugh, rather with his characteristic penetrating look asked me to come and see him at his office after class. Thus began a relationship of teacher–student, *guru–shishya*, mentor–mentee, leading to a friendship that spanned almost two decades. Both Uncle and Auntie have been a blessing to thousands of students and hundreds of faculty in India, particularly in Pune and Bangalore.

Before I continue I want to address two preliminary points. First, growing up as a missionary kid and being overexposed to mission and missionaries from a very young age, I have seen the human side of mission work and it is easy to become sceptical. Dr

Barker not only challenged the scepticism but also enlarged my understanding and experience of missions. He also kept encouraging me to continue to make a contribution to mission studies and practices. When I gave a lecture in 2013, Monty made the effort to come to Oxford and be present. This is what he had to say in his encouraging and sharply educative response: *'Although dense and assuming a fair amount of familiarity with philosophical concepts, even I could follow your general conclusion! I think it was the best I have heard you. You were not combative but more nuanced and persuasive. I am sorry we didn't have any time to go over it in greater detail together...'* I knew he was telling me to be less dense, less combative and more nuanced, and I will miss getting his comments on this occasion.

A few years ago we had a robust conversation about the identity and role of Western missionaries in India. I was arguing how even after 20 years of mission service in a foreign land, a missionary could still choose to remain an outsider. Suddenly the conversation took an unusual personal turn as he turned to face me. 'Then what about me?' he enquired. 'What about my work in India?' I said something to this effect: 'This is exactly what sets you apart from the kind of missionaries I have been describing! Your success in India is precisely because you have become partly Indian. You have a home in Bristol and another in Pune, you have a growing library in both places, and you have Indian paintings on the walls in Pune, even as British art adorns your walls in Bristol. Uncle, you are partly Scotsman, partly English and equally partly Indian!' With his typically raised eyebrow he replied smilingly, 'I guess you could say that and don't forget I am one-eighth Jewish'! I think I spotted a happy glint in his eyes on being called 'partly Indian'! This was in no way a compromise of his Scottish–English roots but rather that he was able to expand and inhabit an Indian world as well. He summed this up on the note he inscribed on a book he gave me on my 32nd birthday entitled *The Argumentative Indian* by Amartya Sen, a well-known Indian economist: *'To an argumentative Indian by an argumentative Indian from an argumentative Scot. Happy Birthday.*

So what marks us out as Indian, Scottish, English, African, or Chinese?

The great paradox: between exclusion and embrace
This is indeed a paradox we see in our world – on the one hand there is a fierce call for unity, togetherness, equality, non-discrimination and universalism, while at the same time practices of exclusion and distrust abound. This same paradox can be seen in missions and mission studies. I want to claim that even the best of Christian missions committed to Jesus' 'love your neighbour as yourself' are unable to overcome the self–other binary. Let's unpack this a bit more from the missionary's perspective. Conceptually, there are three possible relationships between the missionary and the missionised other – (a) the missionary/missionised selves remain differentiated so that the self and the other remain distinct. Here the missionary self continues to differentiate itself from the missionised other and there is no meeting of their different worlds. Let's call this model the *exclusive self*; (b) The second model is where there is a collapse of the missionary self into the missionised other; the term 'going native' has been used to describe this model. Here the missionary loses his or herself and embraces the missionised other so as to be completely eradicated and become one with the missionised other. Let's call this model of missionary self the *embracive self*. These models echo the title of Miroslav Volf's famous book, *Exclusion and Embrace: A Theological Exploration of Identity, Otherness and Reconciliation*.

Rethinking mission as polyhabiting
While in theory these models hold the two extreme positions of utter separation or total immersion, in practice I want to argue that these are impossible states to achieve. One can never keep oneself completely separate and isolated or totally emptied and extinguished.

I would like to argue that all missionary work necessarily falls under a third model even if one does not consciously or explicitly accept this position. In this model there is a degree to which the missionary goes native, but without in any way losing themself. This model brings to the fore the reality of the dynamic engagement between them, which could result in a mutual inhabiting. This calls for a rethinking of identity construction and human engagement and has been academically addressed by identity studies in sociology and anthropology and by theories of the self in philosophy. I am reminded of Charles Taylor's *porous self* as opposed to the Cartesian *buffered self*. But here I would like to explore this model and its underlying theory of the self within mission studies and particularly from the practices modelled in the life and mission of Montagu Barker. I would like to propose that an effective missionary self is necessarily a polyhabiting self – a self that inhabits a plurality of worlds, a prime example of which is Dr Montagu Barker.

Monty was born to a Scottish father and an English mother, and thus one could argue that this polyhabitation or the inhabiting of a plurality of worlds began for him right from birth. Growing up as a Scotsman and then marrying Rosemary, an Englishwoman, and finally working in Bristol, England nurtured this deep dual-belonging to two historical communities and worlds. One could argue that this empowered him to befriend and belong to various other worlds, including the French and the Indian, with both of whom he was a missionary-professor for years.

What we want to learn from Monty's mission practices today is how we can polyhabit in our increasingly multicultural and multi-religious world. I would like to highlight four insights from Monty's mission practices that I will argue constitute the conceptual structure of polyhabiting, which when in play will enable the missionary authentically to polyhabit a plurality of worlds while inviting the other meaningfully to participate in his. It begins with (a) the practice of enquiring, followed by (b) the practice of listening, leading to (c) the practice of inhabiting other worlds and finally to (d) the practice of self-disclosing one's own world that invites the other to participate. These practices are not completely novel and within the discourse on mission studies they have been alluded to by Amos Yong, Professor of Theology at Regent University, particularly in his 2008 book *Hospitality and the Other*.

Writing about American evangelicals and their mission approach, Yong divides them into two camps – the conservatives and the progressives. While the conservatives have 'bemoaned the trend toward multiculturalism and multi-religiosity in America, believing [that] these have nurtured relativism, de-centred Christian faith in the marketplace of competing religions and philosophies, and popularised 'spirituality' rather than authentic religious commitment', the progressives like the Emerging Church movement, he argues, possess a 'less traditional set of approaches to Christian mission'. Rather than 'mark the boundaries', the progressives welcome strangers and engage with 'practices of inclusion', to which one must add the practice of self-disclosing, which brings all this to a missional finale that invites the missionised other to participate in the missionary's world.

I will demonstrate that what Yong theorised were indeed the mission practices of Montagu Barker, thus showing that these practices can constitute an authentic approach to missions crucially relevant in our increasingly multicultural world.

Polyhabiting is living in plural worlds. But how does one live in multiple worlds, or even acquire another world different from one's own? Monty's mission practices give flesh to and reveal how these four insights constitute the mechanism for inhabiting the missionised world while inviting the other to one's own.

Practice of enquiry

The practice of enquiry is not merely asking questions, rather it is a life posture involving authentic seeking. A seeking that is not merely dictated by uncertainties or doubts but rather driven by a reflective knowing of one's limits and a genuine quest to go beyond and know more. Monty's vast personal collection of more than 10,000 volumes is testimony to this seeking. When faced with a different other, instead of marking boundaries or differentiating, he genuinely enquires. This posture of enquiring or asking questions reveals that not only is he willing to accept limits of his own knowledge but also possesses an authentic seeking to expand his own self-understanding and in this process is able to enter into the other's world. In the many conversations I have had with him, he always had questions, not routine, but penetrating on the new things I was reading, processing and believing. Even as I shared, he would often respond with, 'Ah, I can see your point', and would explicitly engage with that idea or thought in light of his own experiences. In spite of his great learning and experience, he was genuinely interested in the other, always open to learn, possessing humility and honesty that made the other welcome.

Practice of listening
In his visits to UBS, Dr Barker's day was not only full of classes he taught but also his diary was full of appointments he had with students and even faculty members who would slip in and out of his study. The dominant image I have of Dr Barker is of him sitting in his chair with a bunch of writing sheets and a pen in his hands, and me sitting on his right side so that I could speak to his better ear, either in UBS or later on in his home in Bristol. His study was full of never-ending piles – piles of papers, newspaper cuttings, files and books. While for most it might resemble complete chaos, to him it was orderly and made perfect sense. Many of those scribbled papers were the remains of a conversation, where he had taken meticulous notes of what the other had shared. Polyhabiting begins with enquiry but has to be necessarily followed with a willingness to listen. For many including me involved with missions, listening is one of the most difficult things to do. We live in a world where everyone is not just speaking, but screaming, and we have lost the spiritual practice of listening. This listening is not a passive activity, but one that actively engages with cross-questions. In this form of active listening, the speaker is both interrogated and judged and

even corrected. Through listening one is able to enter into the other's world and see the world the words reveal.

Practice of inhabiting

While enquiring prepares us to receive the other and listening enables us to enter into the other's world, if we are truly to polyhabit, then we have to inhabit the other's world. It involves travelling, moving into the other's physical world. So one inherits the other's world in all its splendour without in any way giving up one's own world. It is not an *either/or*, rather a *both/and*. Here, Yong's demands for 'visiting other sacred sites and even participating in their liturgies' can be threatening and is therefore often rejected outright. But inhabiting the other's world is not limited to observing the other's spiritual practices, but also clothing oneself with the other's mental, physical and social worlds. It is like being fluent in two or more languages or possessing a dual citizenship. Monty's life of travels, and willingness bodily to experience and clothe himself with the world of the other as epitomised by his maintaining a second home in UBS, Pune for nearly three decades, is living testimony to this practice of inhabiting the other.

Practice of self-disclosure

It is only after the missionary has enquired, listened and inhabited that they earn the right to speak. I wouldn't know the names of the countless thousands in India and elsewhere who have gladly given the right to Dr Montagu Barker to speak into their lives. In our world where missionaries are told to be careful, speak less and often explicitly told to shut up, here we have someone who was gladly bestowed the right to speak! Surely his model of mission has something powerful to offer all of us. But then how should the missionary speak? It is easy to spit out a three-minute Gospel presentation, or whip someone down in an intellectual debate, but presenting Christ so that he is seen takes much more than mere speech. It takes a true conversation within an honest relationship. And this is Monty through and through, building myriads of relationships and yet skilfully navigating through them all. But still how should the missionary speak? The model of speech that Monty followed was one of self-disclosure. He would reveal and make himself visible, warts and all, and in that speech, what God in Christ meant to him could legitimately find space. This form of speech follows the pre-Socratic interpretation of *alethea* as non-concealment rather than propositional truth, as argued by Heidegger in his *Introduction to Metaphysics*. In this self-disclosure, the missionary reveals his world to the listener and invites them to inhabit it. I think humans are attracted to this form of mission, one that is authentic and humble and yet has the most powerful impact on the listener. The missionised other now has the opportunity to enquire, listen to and inhabit the missionary's world. When the missionised other does this, they too polyhabit a plurality of worlds and some call this conversion, although I think we need to go beyond using the language of conversion.

Conclusion

So what does mission as polyhabiting look like? In summary it begins with a spirit of going beyond oneself through the practice of enquiring, then entering into the other's world through the practice of listening, then belonging to the other's world through the practice of inhabiting and finally revealing one's own world through self-disclosure. Through this mechanism one is able to embrace and belong to a plurality of worlds without giving up one's own. It also authentically invites the missionised other to enquire about, listen to and inhabit the missionary's world.

Inhabiting anyone else's world involves decisions and hard choices. I remember twice in my life when I had to take important decisions about inhabiting new worlds. Monty's words arising out of his own experiences have been a shining beacon in enabling me to make the hard choices. Being a missionary kid and growing up in an activism-driven missionary home, after my first visit to the Oxford Centre for Mission Studies in 2005, I had signed off the academic journey thinking it a complete waste of time and not for me. But a 40-minute call from Dr Barker, setting out an argument for why I should return to OCMS and be part of the world of academia and embrace it by completing the PhD that I had begun, was an important step in my reversing my decision. A second instance was when I had finished the PhD and was suddenly faced with a job offer. As many here know, my primary calling is to India and the Hindus. While this job was in India, Monty felt that it would take me away from this calling and the world of the Hindus. He wrote to me saying: 'We wonder if to have organisation X on your CV would in the future jeopardise the very thing you want to pioneer, an approach without prejudice to thinking Hindus. That would be a shame after all the ground you have already been able to possess. Over to you to think that one out!' Dr Montagu Barker in his missional approach not only polyhabited a plurality of worlds but also guided his students, including me, to do the same and it is to him in celebration of his life and work that this lecture is dedicated. Thank you.

Chapter Fifteen
COUNSELLING IN AN INDIAN CONTEXT

As a Westerner I was surprised in 1989 to be asked to contribute to the Pastoral Care and Counselling course for BD students at the Union Biblical Seminary, Pune. I was even more surprised to be asked back each year to contribute yet again. Perhaps my training and practice in the UK, midway between the USA and India, gives me a measure of objectivity regarding some Western models of counselling as well as sensitivity to Eastern values. I have struggled to try to see the training needs of Indian pastors through their eyes while being fully aware of the immense cultural diversity of India itself. In this I have been encouraged and cautioned by my students and pastors.

While wholly approving of the academic priorities of theological colleges, my aim has always been to equip pastors to do their job better by having other dimensions added to their thoughts and skills, but never at the expense of their calling to teach the Word and to care for the people of God. It was in 1994 that I first met Dr I Ben Wati and we discovered immediately a common bond in having given a significant part of our lives serving on the board of a theological college. We both had a major concern that pastoral training programmes should be relevant to people's needs and affect the preaching and 'people skills' of students, while not neglecting scholarly and academic challenges. I came to learn of Dr Ben Wati's commitment to UBS and his concern for the training of pastors for more than 40 years and submit this paper in his honour with the hope that it might stimulate the next generation of teachers and church leaders in India to explore new and Indian directions in pastoral care and counselling.

Pastoral care: changing terminology and context of training
The terms that have been used in the past 150 years to describe the departments involved in training future pastors and ministers included Practical Theology, Pastoral Theology, Pastoral Psychology, Christian Counselling and more recently Biblical Counselling. The first was concerned with relating theological studies to practical issues in Christian living. This was very much the approach of the early Scottish theologians and educators and men such as Alexander Duff and the others of that era who had come from the evangelical wing of the Church of Scotland, which eventually founded the first chair in Practical Theology in the New College in Edinburgh.

Pastoral theology was a more English approach, which tended to begin with specific pastoral problems and seek to bring a theological understanding to the management of such issues. However, by the 1930s, particularly in the United States, there was a grappling with the new disciplines of psychology and psychoanalysis and their relationship to pastoral care. The attempts by Anton Boisen to bring a Christian orientation into such disciplines and to the treatment of mentally ill patients, resulted instead in the introduction of psychology and psychoanalytic thinking into pastoral training programmes. This led to the setting up of departments of pastoral psychology, the study of which which soon became more popular than the more conventional courses in pastoral theology.

By the 1950s, there was an increase in growth of what came to be known as counselling programmes. This due to the popularity of people like Carl Rogers who was actually a divinity student and became the virtual founder and populariser of the counselling movements that shared Christian origins and developed in a humanistic direction. Such was the charisma of Rogers that his teaching and example profoundly influenced the underlying tenets. However, procedures of subsequent counselling approaches may appear to differ from Rogers' own position.

Part of the popularity of the counselling process in the United States arose from the philosophical assumption of self-improvement and inevitable progress, inherent in some Western thinking. Combined with this was the more attractive and cheaper option of counselling, compared with the somewhat rigid, lengthy and costly process of psychoanalysis, which took hold of the psychiatric establishment in the United States in a way which it never did in the rest of the English-speaking world. Christians were drawn to counselling as opposed to psychotherapy with its materialistic and atheistic bias from the theories of Freud.

Accordingly, Christian counselling programmes began to proliferate in the United States associated with names like Narramore and Clinebell. These often developed in Christian schools of divinity. However, conservative Evangelicals in particular perceived the humanistic assumptions and bias of these programmes and the apparent tendency to minimise right and wrong, personal responsibility, guilt, grace, sin, righteousness and redemption, etc. This led to the setting up of counselling programmes, which came to be known as 'biblical' counselling and which acknowledged the existence of mental illness and the need for medical intervention, but rejected much of the other psychological insights and the need for psychotherapy. An extreme example is that of Jay Adams who re-translated the New Testament from the point of view of the *'nouthetic counsellor'*. This New Testament has an index at the back that lists all the psychological and spiritual afflictions of mankind with an appropriate text, which could be described as the 'biblical remedy'.

Counselling within an Indian Context

A comprehensive and critical review of the multitude of counselling programs is contained in Dr Roger Hurding's book, *The Tree of Healing*, first published in 1985 under the title *Roots and Shoots – a Guide to Counselling and Psychotherapy*.

The only author I know who has sought to reflect widely upon the philosophical and psychological material that has emerged from the West, in addition to counselling and therapy from an Indian point of view, is Sudhir Kakar. He trained as a psychologist and therapist under Erickson and has published several books since 1979 when he wrote *Identity and Adulthood*. He practised both in Delhi and the United States and his books are available in the West; some of them were put into an omnibus edition under the title *The Indian Psyche* in which he engages in conversation with Ramin Jahan Begloo. In this volume he describes, in a brief autobiographical sketch, the struggle to combine his Indian roots with the 'liberating knowledge' of the West that resulted in his writings. He describes the warm, encompassing security of the joint family of his childhood and the implicit confidence he had in the collective wisdom of the family elders. However, the underlying awareness of the oppressive atmosphere of that family suddenly erupted as he set sail to the UK. It was his meeting with Erickson, who was the great writer on the subject of identity, which helped him deal with his own identity crisis. To some extent, his books speak especially to the 'Indian middle-class torn in its orientation between East and West in conflict between European and Indian models and values'.

Kakar's writings deal very effectively with issues such as family, identity, marriage and sexual intimacy in a way that I have not seen covered in other texts coming from Indian authors. There are textbooks on counselling, but there is little that is specific to the Indian situation. One such textbook is that by Prof S Narayana Rao, who was formerly Professor, Chairman of the Department of Psychology and Dean of the School of Social and Behavioural Sciences in Sri Venkateswarar University College, Tirupati. He eventually became the principal of this college and was awarded a special honour for the best book published when he published his book *Counselling Psychology* in 1981. The second edition was published in 1992 entitled *Counselling and Guidance*. This is a very comprehensive book on the literature published in the West on counselling. From time to time there is a brief note on differences between the Western and Indian situations and attitudes. Considerable space is given to youth counselling, but the emphasis is very much upon achieving academic potential and vocational guidance. Brief mention is made of the kind of difficulties experienced in marriages from different perspectives as well as of social attitudes to marriage. There is no advice given except that non-directive individual counselling might be the best approach towards marriage difficulties in India. Indeed, the book ends on the somewhat despairingly pessimistic note that in spite of departments of psychology being established in the 1950s and 1960s in Indian universities, and in spite of there being counsellors in some of the Christian colleges in Bombay, 'Counselling as a professional field of service is yet to emerge in India. This is because firstly there are no employment opportunities for trained counsellors and secondly there are no qualified or trained personnel. This is a vicious circle which needs to be broken, if we want to progress.'

In fact, there is rather more available than Prof Rao seems to be aware of. For example, in Nur Manzil Hospital in Lucknow, the Christian psychiatric unit was founded more than 50 years ago. The Christian counselling centre of Vellore also has a long history and the book *Indian Case Studies in Therapeutic Counselling* by B J Prashantham, published in 1975, is still one of the major texts referred to by theological students. Dr Prashantham hoped to publish further to include more mature reflections on grappling with the realities of pastoral problems within Indian family and marital life, having indicated the urgent need for literature on the subject in 1975.

There are other counselling centres and training programmes within India. One such is a new two-year programme at Lonavala run by the Sadhana Institute drawing from the teaching staff of Jnana-Deepa Vidyapeeth. This course has a highly philosophical and somewhat esoteric bias, but is an attempt to explore cross-cultural and interdisciplinary approaches involving Christian faith, Indian tradition, scientific psychology and Eastern wisdom. At this stage its relevance for training pastors would seem to be limited.

The complexity of Indian society

Part of the problem would seem to be the complexity of Indian society. Counselling clearly does take place, largely along Western models, within the middle-class metro cultures of Mumbai, Kolkata, etc. I suspect that this is largely limited to people from a Christian background. Although there are books on healing and therapy drawing upon Eastern philosophies, these would involve some commitment to the philosophical bases of such practices as yoga and Zen meditation. They are mainly focused upon self-awareness rather than focusing on specific areas of conflict and their resolution, which is inherent in most Western therapy and counselling techniques. The fact that the burgeoning middle-class is trying to grapple with an Indian background and a Western foreground may bring about a change here. There is a possible emergence of a global 'healing culture' with a 'pick and mix' approach to counselling.

Even when dealing with Christians one needs to be aware of different cultures in India, each having its own values. Therefore it is most unlikely that any one counselling programme will meet the needs or speak to the lives of the people of all cultures. The fact remains that there are very specific areas of crisis that recur constantly within the pastoral context and which require understanding and counselling from Christian pastors. For example, depression is nowadays becoming a common life experience.

Some forms of depression are eminently treatable, but ignorance, fear and a false spirituality prevents or delays the treatment of many within Indian churches, where either depression is thought not to exist or is always attributed entirely to spiritual causes. Other areas of crisis in Indian society are the increasing suicide rate (particularly among newly married women), physical, sexual and emotional abuse, drug abuse and addiction, the menace of AIDS, marital violence and oppression of women.

Some recent assignments from the Christian pastors and workers registered as extension students in UBS gave a dismal account of domestic misery and women 'weeping silently'. To go to a counsellor or pastor would in many cases be viewed as disloyal or shameful.

In my nine years of listening to students and others in parts of India, I have been aware of the recurrent conflict of students who begin the story with, 'I love my parents dearly... They are good parents...' but then go on to describe abuse, violence and mental cruelty within the family. There are deep social and philosophical differences between East and West, which make the approaches of Western counselling programmes unlikely to have much impact on these issues. There needs to be more intense discussion of how to deal with family problems, where shame is felt as part of the fear of public criticism rather than guilt as a result of moral failure. In the West, an awareness of self-identity is seen as coming from the stripping of all extras to reveal 'one's true self'. In the East self is more often discovered as all the ingredients of one's family, past and culture are added to identity. The concept of 'a good family' would cause perplexity in the West, but in the East carries with it the notion of an individual's being and success coming from the kinship, support and heritage of a large number of people, as opposed to individual merits and the rising above the limitations and difficulties.

In 1991 there appeared a two-volume compendium of appraisals of research done on families with problems in India published by the Tata Institute of Social Studies. This is an authoritative and illuminating publication. In one of the chapters it is admitted that 'teaching new patterns of communication within marriage and family, would necessitate challenging the hierarchy between generations and spouses and bring major considerations of the structure of the family, that go far beyond the scope of a marital counsellor'. It is here that training communities such as UBS, with which I am most familiar, should turn their attention.

Possible ways forward
Within evangelicalism, there is a strong heritage of pastoral care and what was called 'case work' by the Puritans. It is from this

stable that modern counselling derives some of its impetus. There are three components: preaching, fellowship and specific dealing with cases by pastors, which would now come under the rubric of counselling. This order will remain in our minds as we look ahead.

1. The preaching of the Word

The preaching was both doctrinal and experiential. There was a belief that the Word of God, properly handled, could speak to the hearts and minds with behaviour modification. The bulk of counselling was probably received at congregational level through preaching and only the residue of 'difficult cases' was dealt with in pastoral visitation and 'casework'. Much is talked today about getting back to expository preaching. However, expository preaching that does not become topical and touch upon the issues that regularly recur in counselling is not truly feeding and nourishing the people of God. No doubt this is dealt with in homiletics classes in theological colleges, but it seems to me that there is scope for more rigorous attention to this issue. Preaching is an agent of change and some of the preoccupation with counselling arises from the lack of application of much preaching.

2. Fellowship groups

There is extensive literature on the influence and power of small-group meetings for prayer, Bible study and fellowship. The Puritan Praying Society, Methodist class meeting and the cottage prayer meeting are all examples. Such groups have gone down in history as origins of revivals. Much more important has been their influence in caring for each other and pastoring those who would now present more readily for counselling. This is a theme that was explored by Thomas Oden in his book *The New Pietism* (when discussing the encounter groups of the 1960s and 1970s, which were part of the counselling movements of that time). There is a distrust of house fellowships within some mainline denominations, which deprives the family of God of these resources for pastoral care and spiritual growth (Heb 10:24,25). There are dangers, but unless we encourage students to think more adventurously and also to ensure proper safeguards, we encourage pastor-dependent churches and exhaust such counselling resources as they may have. Pastoral care and counselling courses should make special efforts to encourage mutual counselling within the fellowship rather than become overdependent on specialist counselling programmes.

3. Psychological understanding

It is foolish to turn our backs on the understanding of personality, family relationships and psychological processes that have accumulated over the past decades. The fact that this material has been used to diminish personal responsibility does not mean it should be abandoned. The effects of genetic factors on personality, sexuality and emotional responses need to be acknowledged by Christians. However, the fact that there may be a genetic predisposition does not absolve us from moral responsibility in how we deal with that. The systems arising from psychological observations need to be questioned, but the objective data may be incorporated within our preaching, pastoring and counselling, for example in helping those going through major life events such as birth, bereavement, loss and change.

4. Agents of change and healing

The Western world looks for programmes and techniques that could be taken up, used, packaged and sold as a source of income. The fact that there are hundreds of different counselling programmes, and even Christian counselling programmes, all with their manuals, worksheets and advanced courses, indicates that there are probably a few simple ingredients common to all these and to many other healing techniques that are well-established in Eastern philosophy and healing traditions. There is significant literature on the subject. What is necessary is critical evaluation of what truly promotes Christian maturity as opposed to just a sense of well-being. Unfortunately people seek quick results from techniques. However, the scrutiny of new experiences of the Spirit, special deliverances and the latest secret to holy living is likely to meet hostility, suspicion and fear in some evangelical circles. An examination of psychological factors in Christian experience should be part of our training of pastors because so many people whom I see for special counselling are those who have felt let down and betrayed by various 'spiritual' remedies that have proved ineffective. Some of this I have explored elsewhere in dealing with the experience of inner healing.

5. The Wounded Healer

Some of the best pastors and counsellors are those who themselves have gone through times of deep personal pain. Many counselling programmes enforce intense self-scrutiny as part of the training of the counsellor. This can be destructive and nothing should be embarked upon that cannot be followed up and for which responsibility cannot be taken. However, within the Serampore course on pastoral care and counselling, there is ample opportunity for looking at the processes leading to depression following bereavements and broken relationships in such a way that students can see themselves and learn something of their own mental processes and backgrounds. This, however, means that the person engaged in such activity must be prepared and available to respond to the counselling needs of the students themselves arising from such teaching. In my nine years of teaching in UBS, the number of hours spent on specific counselling of students has been two to three times more than the hours spent on all the teaching, faculty and preaching commitments. Many students seem to have deep emotional problems, of which they were only partially aware previously. Others were aware of difficulties but have never dared to share with others. Some have been frankly ill from a psychiatric point of view and were in fact referred to a psychiatrist or advised to seek medication from the doctor. One of the most fulfilling aspects of teaching over a period of years is the opportunity to see the progress of the students themselves while in college, then meet them in various contexts while involved in ministry in various parts of India. It is my strong recommendation that anyone who takes on the task of teaching counselling at this level should have a commitment to that kind of follow-through and follow-up ministry. There is an enormous divergence of cultural differences, abilities, gifts and experiences as well as comprehension of psychological concepts within the student body. There may therefore be a place for more advanced exploration of pastoral needs and counselling approaches within the curriculum. To some extent this is catered for by the optional course on marriage and family counselling for the final-year students at UBS. However, exposing hidden wounds and conflicts can be unsettling and potentially destructive, if not handled sensitively.

6. Seminary colloquia

There is a dearth of serious academic discussion which is rooted in pastoral experience regarding pastoral problems and their handling within a specifically Indian situation. In the magazine *India Today*, 31 December 1996, there is an article entitled 'The Search for Intimacy'. It was a review of the results of a questionnaire on marital problems. As usual, there was plenty of information, some analysis, but little help. It would seem to me that Faculty could begin to look at special subjects for an in-depth discussion on issues such as promoting communication within the family; how to tackle sexual education within conservative congregations; training youth leaders in identifying and helping abused children; how to encourage and support women in oppressive families without making their situation worse. As far as I am aware, there is little on tackling these issues within the evangelical community. The approach by the women's liberation bodies may be valiant, but often provokes an even more negative response from those who most need to change their attitudes. Such colloquia properly edited could be valuable resources for future pastors and church leaders.

7. Post-graduate seminars

Students doing a BD course usually have very limited experience of pastoral problems and the issues involved. Some have been pastors and this shows in the kind of response they have to the course, but for many the pastoral care and counselling course is theoretical. One's aim is to give them a structure and guidelines with some shafts of understanding of themselves to enable them to begin to cope with pastoral situations and the kind of counselling demanded of them when they graduate. However, it is in the first five years of pastoral ministry that the young pastor makes mistakes, often becomes overwhelmed by pastoral demands and counselling situations and decides that a more limited and sometimes better paid position within some para-church organisation is preferable to pastoral ministry. I believe that the theological college could offer a unique ministry to its former students by deliberately having gatherings of graduates who are in pastoral ministry and Christian work where there could be 'case conferences' and the opportunity for more in-depth seminars in discussions relating to pastoral care and counselling. Perhaps conferences can be arranged at the college itself with a subsidy for travel. However, there is some advantage in former students in their own localities meeting together so that there is at least a familiarity with each other that encourages greater openness and preparedness to be vulnerable and learn as a group. The on-going pastoral care for each other in their own area could be further enhanced. My experience in Bangalore with an inter-church pastoral care weekend confirmed me in the view that this could work in India as well as in the West. One of the most memorable of such occasions was a meeting of 300 ministers who all knew each other as part of an evangelical fellowship within the Church of Scotland. The in-depth discussion of half a dozen insoluble counselling scenarios was viewed as one of the most practical sessions they had had in their years of annual pastoral conferences.

8. Pastor/counsellor/psychiatrist

These three groups of 'helpers' of people are different in terms of their world view, their contact situation, their relationship, their resources and their goal. The pastor sees people as God's creation, the counsellor relates to them as his clients and the psychiatrist as his patients.

In the contact situation the pastor sees them as being part of the fellowship, belonging in the church, the counsellor may see them as part of a group and relate to them in an interview process, and the psychiatrist would see them in his consulting room as a patient and may offer them a prescription.

In terms of relationships the pastor would see those he cares for as a brother or sister with needs, the counsellor would see the client as one with problems, and the psychiatrist would see them as a patient with an illness.

In terms of resources the pastor will be preaching the Word of God and administering sacraments within the fellowship. The counsellor will bring his experience and skill and the personality of a counsellor. The psychiatrist would bring different techniques, resources and medication within the clinic or hospital setting.

In terms of the goal the pastor's aim is to present the person 'mature in Christ Jesus'. The counsellor's aim is to promote happiness and achievement of potential, and the psychiatrist's aim is to relieve suffering and to restore function.

There is much in common between the activities of the pastor, counsellor and psychiatrist. However, the more we move the centre of our activity from pastoring into specific counselling, the less we will be able to do the things that only the pastor can do. The pastor can learn much from the counselling movements in the rules of good behaviour and responsible attitudes within caring relationships. But at the end of the day, if we are training pastors, then we must keep clearly the vision of the pastor. Even the Christian counsellor is constrained by the limitations of the semi-professional stance that is necessary. The pastor can acquire counselling skills, but the church needs pastors first and foremost, whose goal is to produce men and women who are mature in Christ Jesus.

Behavioural sciences should illumine our pastoring skills and caring. Our aim should be to encourage, enable and empower communities of caring, not produce experts in counselling. The setting up of counselling specialists in churches and localities can have the effect of de-skilling gifted counsellors in fellowships who would never wear a counsellor's badge. Specialist counselling courses may well have their place. But I would make a plea for the training and on-going support of pastors and church leaders who are learning to care for and counsel the household of God, mindful of psychological research and insights, but determined to do so within the fellowship and in a way that is sensitive to the Indian context.

Chapter Sixteen
MADNESS: THE COST OF MISSION?
A STUDY OF WILLIAM & DOROTHY CAREY

There is a great need for those in mission oversight continually to review the pastoral care of their workers. William Carey provides an example of a gifted, visionary pioneer missionary whose wife passed through what seems to us now unnecessary suffering. Care of family and colleagues and a willingness to be open to both encouragement and correction within a team could prevent much breakdown among mission leaders.

Introduction

'Madness, the cost of mission?' was one of several titles considered for a book on the life of Dorothy Carey by James Beck, eventually entitled *Dorothy Carey, The Tragic and Untold Story of Mrs William Carey.* No doubt it was prudent to alter the title for the purposes of marketing and to appeal to the Christian community. When a film was made about the Careys, based partly on this account, the title chosen was *Candle in the Dark,* which certainly conveys the double meaning of the darkness into which William Carey sought to bring the light of the Gospel and the darkness of mind and spirit that engulfed Dorothy's life and even threatened William Carey's own mental and spiritual equilibrium.

I have written elsewhere on the subject of emotional and family stresses within ministry. The topic that I wish to deal with in this paper is the ordinary stresses that compound the cross-cultural pressures and relative isolation experienced by many involved in mission. I have taken William Carey as a paradigm because elements of his story are well-known and his place within mission leadership well documented. He has of course special significance for the Indian context and therefore seemed an appropriate example from which to draw observations at the conclusion of this consultation at Union Biblical Seminary, Pune on 'Issues in mission leadership'. However, no account of Carey's life and ministry can omit a reference to the sufferings of his wife, Dorothy. James Beck's account of her 'tragic and untold story' makes the point very tellingly that it is not sufficient just to comment on the pressures upon mission leaders, but that the mental health of their associates in mission, including family and colleagues, must also be acknowledged.

In the preparation of this paper I have found it difficult to discover documentation in biographical and autobiographical accounts of Indian mission leaders. There is material recorded on the lives of Western expatriates working in India, but few personal accounts of mental health issues by indigenous mission leaders themselves. There may well be much more information in accounts in the vernacular languages as opposed to English, but I wonder if there is not also a reluctance to discuss conflicts and struggles that have resulted in temporary or even permanent mental breakdown. I have no doubt that the issues of challenging life events, personality conflict, social and cultural differences, family expectations and needs, and struggles with the apparently inscrutable ways of God in spite of His apparently clear call, exist in East and West, although the cultural expression and reflection on these issues may differ.

This was brought home to me recently when reading the account of the CPS Ashram here in Pune. This Ashram arose out of the desire of the Rev Jack Winslow and other Indian nationals to establish a 'more thoroughly Indian' religious community. Men like C F Andrews and Verrier Elwin were also involved in the early days. Here was an extraordinary and innovative attempt to pioneer a specifically Indian approach to mission, but from early on until its demise 50 years later it was beset with struggles and conflict, although these are only obliquely referred to. It was an experiment that other leaders also attempted, such as Narayan

Vaman Tilak and E Stanley Jones. There may well have been reasons why all of these failed in some measure, but what is of interest to me is that the emotional cost associated with these struggles is only briefly and indirectly alluded to in spite of the immense personal and spiritual investment involved in these enterprises. I have not come across any account of how the *Indian* members of the Ashrams were affected. Was their investment any less, or the emotional cost and sense of loss any less painful? I therefore crave your patience and understanding, and hopefully enlightenment, as I seek to reflect on issues in mission leadership and mental health.

Treasures in jars of clay

The Apostle Paul in his second letter to the Corinthians reminds us that whatever our calling and role in mission, we carry the Gospel as though in jars of clay. Every Christian is called to bear witness to the Gospel of Jesus Christ. Whether this ministry is perceived as being in leadership or in servanthood, Paul reminds us that we are all subject to the same psychological, emotional and physical ailments as the rest of humanity. We see this exemplified in the life of the prophet Elijah when the writer of the Book of Kings describes the limits of his endurance and the crushing depression that he suffered even in the middle of apparent victory.

Much has been written suggesting Dorothy Carey's weaknesses as a person and her apparent lack of commitment to her husband's vision and call. In fact, the human pressures to which she was subjected in the first two years after her arrival in India would serve as a classic textbook illustration on the causation of clinical depression. Physical exhaustion, chronic ill-health, financial insecurity and a strange, not to say alien environment, would all be looked upon as obvious factors leading to impaired mental health. While these could nowadays be considered part of the ordinary experience of any cross-cultural missionary going into a pioneer situation, in Dorothy's case there were also additional factors. There was the discovery that both she and her husband had been misled, not to say deceived, by the very person who had persuaded her in spite of her expressed fears to accompany her husband to India. She had left her family behind, except for a sister who accompanied them. She discovered that their savings were virtually worthless, and within two months she had three moves of home forced upon her by virtue of financial difficulties. There was then a year of chronic ill health, uncertainty regarding their future in India, followed by the loss of her sister, four more moves of house, isolation in the jungle surrounded by tigers, severe and recurrent fever and dysentery in all the family, and finally the death of her five-year-old son less than two years after arriving in Calcutta.

It is well recognised that one major life event can normally be coped with. When two life events occur within a matter of months this is likely to cause impairment of function. Three or more major life events within a space of two years often prove more than the ordinary human being can cope with without experiencing some measure of depression. Dorothy had far in excess of the normal quota by anyone's standards. This, coupled with her perception of a husband who did not sympathise with her situation (and certainly he showed little evidence in his writings of understanding her position), in my opinion led to the irrational and apparently unfounded pathological suspicion of a husband who did not care for her and therefore was interested in other women.

Within four months she became increasingly insane with profound depression and the pathological suspicion of her husband's infidelity, and was a cause of great anxiety to William Carey himself. Within five months of her son's death she was pregnant again but the birth of a further child was associated with a deterioration rather than an amelioration in her mental symptoms. William himself records his own bleak and depressive rumination and in February 1795, just over two months after his son's death, he wrote: 'This is indeed the valley of the shadow of death to me, except that my soul is much more insensible than John Bunyan's Pilgrim; oh, what would I give for a kind, sympathetic friend such as I had in England to whom I could open my heart.' Subsequent entries make comments such as, 'Oh, what a load is a barren heart, I feel a little forlorn pleasure in thinking over the time that has passed and drown some of my heaviness by writing to my friends in England... I sometimes walk in my garden and try to pray to God, and if I pray at all it is in the solitude of a walk... Soon gross darkness returned; spoke a word or two to a Mohammedan upon things of God, but I feel as bad as they... Much to complain of, another such dead soul I think scarcely exists in the world. I can only compare myself to one banished from all his friends and wandering in an irksome solitude... I have been very unhappy ... My soul was overwhelmed with depression.' Only in June, almost five months later, does he make reference to the 'very sore trials in my own family from a quarter which I forbear to mention'.

I have always resisted the request to include details of my patients unless I have been given specific permission to refer to them. But, as Dr Marjory Foyle in her excellent book, *Honourably Wounded*, makes clear, there is a significant amount of psychiatric morbidity among those involved in mission. Often this is referred to as some mysterious physical illness, and accompanied by fruitless investigations and medication. While probably less frequent in those who eventually achieve leadership roles, this is far from infrequent among those in pioneering situations. A favourite way of dealing with such people in a discreet way is to arrange for a sabbatical or a refresher course. If recovery is achieved, well and good. If not, then the person is quietly transferred or leaves.

None of us can ever say that we will not be assailed during our own ministries by affliction, torment, persecution or the proximity of one emotional challenge following too closely upon another. Leaders in mission are no exception to this. Dr Marjorie Foyle, for some years director of Nur Manzil Psychiatric Clinic in Lucknow, following her retirement toured many mission hospitals throughout India to bring awareness of these issues and alert mission leaders to the fragility of the clay vessels in which the treasure of the Gospel is contained.

Looking at ourselves realistically

In chapter 12 of his letter to the Roman Church, Paul asks that the members of the Church should not 'think of themselves more highly' than they ought, but rather think of themselves 'with sober judgement'. He goes on to describe various forms of ministry and gifts.

When people preach or talk on this passage attention is usually given to identifying one's own particular gifts and recognising these in the context of the fellowship. However, I do not think we can avoid the command to have a good, long, hard, realistic look at ourselves. This must include reflection on our own personalities. Even if we do not recognise our habitual reactions, other people do. When we have some official leadership status, how available are we for others to draw alongside and assist us in realistic appraisal of our own gifts?

It has become quite fashionable to subject members of organisations and institutions to personality profiling that outlines the various types of personalities and their likely interaction with other people and situations. I have a certain scepticism as to how helpfully these tests are applied or understood. Nevertheless they do draw attention to the very different ways in which individuals within a team or organisation can react to confrontation, decision making and the exercise of leadership roles.

It may seem somewhat presumptuous to reflect on William Carey's personality. To read back into diaries and records of events can at best be conjecture and I have no wish to denigrate the greatness, vision and humanity of Carey. There can be no doubt that he was a person of immense ability, drive and wholehearted application, which others recognised and then willingly followed his leadership. There is no doubt either that he learnt from errors of judgement that he made, notably in his reliance upon Dr Thomas whose importunity fired Carey's precipitate departure for India in 1793, which ended when Thomas and Carey, along with his older son, were peremptorily told to leave the ship at the first port of call and return home. There were already indications that Dr Thomas was not a wholly reliable character but Carey seemed ill-disposed to listen to his wife's hesitations and the captain's reasons for refusing to allow them further passage on his ship. In fact, Thomas was himself a rather unstable manic-depressive who was subsequently confined to a psychiatric hospital compulsorily for a period of time.

In the area of Carey's marriages one cannot doubt his feelings of affection and his intent to love his wives (he had three altogether) and his children. However, when he married Dorothy he was not yet 20 years of age and she was several years his senior. She was his employer's sister-in-law but illiterate. She was only too aware of his passion for learning and languages, albeit self-taught. She hesitated to accept his proposal of marriage on the grounds that, 'William, books speak to you, they don't speak to me.' Their marriage certificate was signed by William Carey, but she signified her assent with a cross, suggesting that she was unable even to write her name.

Dorothy Carey died in December 1807. In his letter to his sisters in January 1808 he told them of Mrs Carey's death, and informed them that he had already proposed to a Danish noblewoman who had accepted. Her Christian character as well as her financial resources were mentioned in the letter. They were married exactly five months after the first Mrs Carey's death. They had known each other since he came to Serampore seven years previously and there is no doubt that she shared in his work in a way that Dorothy had not been able to do since coming to India. When his second wife died at the end of May 1821, Carey spoke of it as 'the greatest domestic loss that a man can sustain'. In a letter he wrote: 'My life is solitary and melancholy. I shall, I think, endeavour to marry again after some time, but at present I know not where to look for a woman who would be a suitable partner for me.' He did indeed remarry and was lovingly nursed by his third wife when he died twelve years later.

It might seem harsh to judge someone like Carey by the standards and attitudes of a subsequent generation, but the model of Carey and others of similar mould has too often been used by mission leaders to justify a single-mindedness and dedication to the call of God, which sometimes paid little attention to the needs of others working with them, quite apart from those of their spouses or families.

The experiences of Narayan Vaman Tilak and Pandita Ramabai in dealing with colleagues who saw issues differently from themselves are well known. The story of Amy Carmichael of Dohnavur gives a further illustration of the potential for conflict and emotional turbulence when mission leaders seeking to pursue a vision, encounter boards and colleagues who seem to challenge that vision and their authority. An interesting study of Amy Carmichael was included in a book by Gaius Davies entitled *Genius, Grief and Grace*. Amy's story of the 'Dohnavur family', as she liked to call it, was entitled *Golden Cord*. In his perceptive study, however, Dr Davies summarises his analysis of her personality with the following comment under the subtitle 'Disentangling the Gold Cord': 'There were perhaps three major strands in her temperament which together made her the peculiar genius that she was. The first was her perfectionism; the second her ability to turn every crisis into a drama; and the third her mystical devotion to her Lord and Master.' When asked to speak on the subject of perfectionism to a Christian community many years ago, I used Amy Carmichael as an example of someone whose perfectionist personality created problems for herself and even more for her fellow workers. She liked to call them 'family' but often the family members had to leave because of the burdens she imposed upon them when they questioned her need to dominate. In the room, unknown to me, was an elderly lady who had served with Amy Carmichael at Dohnavur. She smilingly but ruefully agreed with my assessment.

Perhaps it is perfectionism that is one of the most potentially damaging personality traits among leaders. It often arises out of a deep personal insecurity masked by high intelligence, giftedness, visionary insight and a thoroughness that inevitably fast-tracks a person into leadership roles. They may then perceive the advent of other equally able colleagues as a threat, and differences of opinion and approach quickly become sources of conflict and even bitterness and cause splits within an organisation, which initially had seemed full of blessing and promise. Such situations do not happen suddenly. There is usually adequate warning building up over some years but a lack of closeness to the situation by those who have oversight of the mission and a mistaken reluctance to confront issues may lead to a departure of some from the battlefield, leaving others permanently wounded.

Lack of consideration – and the hindrance of prayers

It may be significant that it is the Apostle Peter in chapter 3 of his first general Letter who, when talking about the relationships of wives and husbands, has a special word for praying husbands. Peter with his outstanding leadership gifts and a special calling from the Lord, so often got it wrong but he seems to have learnt from each bitter experience. We know nothing about his relationship with his wife but I wonder if this comment in his Letter reflects something of his own personal experience when he specifically reminds husbands to show consideration for their wives lest their prayers be hindered. It is unlikely that Peter's impetuosity, so evident in the Gospel accounts and in Acts, was not reflected in his personal relationships. It can only be conjecture, but perhaps his wife had had a rather tough time with her husband and Peter had had to learn the hard way what 'submit to one another out of reverence for Christ' really meant in practical terms in family relationships and ministry.

We have already referred to the marriage of William and Dorothy Carey. There is no indication that Dorothy was unhappy or that William had cause for complaint during the first 13 years of their marriage, which were spent in England. She seems to have been contented and effective as a Baptist pastor's wife, although this role was not what she had expected when she first married him. They had coped with the births of several children and the loss of two children after birth. There is no record of disagreement until William announced his personal call to go to India there and then in the company of Dr Thomas in the spring of 1793, when she was already some months pregnant. She expressed her misgivings, her fears and the fact that although William felt called, she had had no personal call herself. The rest of the story has already been touched upon and is more fully documented in James Beck's account. In a personal letter to myself written by a direct descendant of William and Dorothy, reference is made to Dorothy having been spoken of in 'a hushed voice and referred to with an element of shame and a lack of sympathetic understanding' by members of the family for several generations. It is this lack of understanding and the seeming inability of William Carey to put himself in his wife's situation and see things from her point of view, that to my mind lies at the heart of the story.

As I read Paul's Letter to the Ephesian Church, it seems to me that he is saying that in all our family relations and particularly in the husband–wife relationship, subjection to each other means putting ourselves in the other person's shoes and seeking to see things from their point of view. I would suggest that this is the meaning of the Greek word *hupotasso*, submit, in this particular context and that this is what Peter is advocating in his Letter. Certainly Dorothy did not feel that William could see things from her point of view, and although she accompanied him to India and there were times when the relationship was harmonious even in the middle of their troubles, there is little evidence that he was able to communicate his attempts to understand her fears and feelings. Even when he does reflect upon his family situation when they had to undertake arduous journeys in difficult situations, his private reflection (hopefully not shared with the family) was: 'had some little enjoyment of God today, but travelling with a family is a great hindrance to holy spiritual meditation ... Much mercy has followed us all through this journey and considering the very weak state of my wife we have been supported beyond expectation. Travelling in general I have always found unfriendly to the progress of the divine life in my soul. But travelling with a family more particularly so.' Not an encouraging note in the light of what was to follow.

Dr C Barnabas published a paper in the Indian Journal of Missiology in 1998 entitled *Problems of Missionary Families, Historical Examples.* May I recommend this paper as a salutary reminder to all in leadership that those of us who are married have a dual calling, namely to serve the Lord and also to care for our families. So often I have heard mission leaders state that their calling and responsibilities within mission meant that they had to leave the care of their wife and especially the children in the Lord's hands. One mission leader with real potential recently commented that one of the advantages of an arranged marriage with its possibly more limited emotional and personal intimacy between the couple was that the servant of the Lord was 'more able and freer to develop intimacy with the Lord'. By contrast, Richard Holloway, former Bishop of Edinburgh, has stated that 'the marriage relationship should reflect the relationship of the persons of the divine Trinity in so far as this is possible by human analogy', in showing 'an experience of surrender without domination, service without compulsion, love without conditions – reflecting all the truths of God's love and grace'.

Wives of Fame is the title of a book by Edna Healey examining three wives of internationally famous individuals, one of whom is Mary Livingstone. The author describes, as does Dr Barnabas, the neglect by David Livingstone of his wife. He left her alone for long periods and then when he did ask her to accompany him on a particularly hazardous journey by canoe, she was already pregnant and weak and she gave birth to their fifth child in the canoe in the heart of unknown territory surrounded by jungle. His mother-in-law upbraided him for his thoughtlessness and callousness in this action. He appears to have paid no attention to this but displeased with Mary's frequent pregnancies he concluded that travelling thereafter with his family was better avoided. Even to this day members of the Moffat family, descendants of Mary Livingstone's brother, express reservations when speaking of the achievements of their distant but still famous relative and missionary leader.

There are workaholics within ministry and leadership and mission history is increasingly prepared to record the cost if not of insanity, certainly in terms of deep unhappiness and misery, in the homes of many missionary pioneers and leaders. My own experience is that twice as many wives of Christian ministers and missionaries are referred to me professionally, as ministers and missionaries themselves.

There are other issues such as the care of one's children and the educational needs of children whose parents are working in remote areas. This is a particular problem in India and causes much heartache to the parents. Dr Foyle in her book makes reference to these issues and I have no ready solution to offer, except that whatever statistics there may be to show the benefits of boarding school or home education, statistics do not help in the evaluation of the individual child's need and capacity to cope with absence from parents and the rigours or benefits of boarding school. Understanding on the part of mission boards and leaders and attempts to facilitate communication within separated families would do much to alleviate the guilt of parents and facilitate the return of some parents to mission, even if they had to withdraw temporarily for family reasons.

All belonging to all the others
In the passage we have already referred to Paul, speaking to the Roman Christians, reminds them that although we may have different functions and different gifts, in Christ we form one body and 'each member belongs to all the others'. It is a phrase repeated in some Christian traditions every time we approach the Lord's table and partake of Communion together. In the Church to which I belong, when assisting during the Communion service I am struck by the fact that the hands that are held out to receive the bread and wine are so different. Each person kneels and holds out their hands. Some are gnarled and arthritic, others are young and smooth, some are ingrained with the soil of the fields in the cracks and creases, others are pale with polished nails. Some are the hands of those who are leaders with recognised functions

within the church, others are the hands of people with no defined function or leadership role within the fellowship. Yet within that company of Christ's people and within the wider community of Christ's church, all have equal status and belong to each other. It is the neglect of this aspect of Biblical teaching that seems to me to be one of the greatest dangers for Christian leaders, whether in mission or in other spheres of service.

It was John Stott's experience of 35 years of travelling to many countries and observing the church and its leadership, that led him to say: 'Our model of leadership is often shaped more by culture than by Christ. Yet many models of leadership are incompatible with the servant imagery exhibited by the Lord Jesus. Nevertheless, these alien cultural models are often transplanted uncritically into the church and its hierarchy. In Africa it is the tribal chief, in Latin America the machismo (exaggerated masculinity) of the Spanish male, in South Asia the Confucian legacy of the teacher's unchallengeable authority, and in Britain the British Raj mentality, the overbearing pride associated with the period of British rule until Indian Independence in 1947.' Stott concludes by quoting a Scottish Presbyterian minister, James Stalker, writing a hundred years ago: 'When I first was settled in a church, I discovered a thing of which nobody had told me and which I had not anticipated, but which proved a tremendous aid in doing the work of the ministry. I fell in love with my congregation. I do not know how otherwise to express it. It was as genuine a blossom of the heart as any which I had ever experienced. It made it easy to do anything for my people.'

I do not have the length of years, the magisterial authority or the international exposure of John Stott. I do, however, have almost 40 years' experience of exploring in depth and at length the thoughts, suffering and despair of many Christian leaders who had never thought that they would have to sit in the psychiatrist's chair. I taught for many years that the most vulnerable pastor is the pastor who has himself or herself no pastor. My experience in coming to India over the past years has convinced me that this is as true in South Asia as in the West. Leadership within the church, and perhaps even more so leadership in mission, can lead men and women into situations of deep isolation and loneliness. Unless deliberate measures are taken to ensure their own pastoral oversight and links with those who care for them, then isolation, exhaustion, breakdown and an overwhelming sense of failure may ensue. We may recall the experience of Moses who was saved from probable breakdown by the timely counsel of his father-in-law, Jethro.

The key issue is the need for all of us, and especially leaders in isolated or pioneering situations, to have a network of others whom we can trust and allow to love us sufficiently to be able to challenge as well as encourage. The writer to the Hebrew Christians is insistent that we should actually look for ways in which we can meet up with others to be provoked to love and good works. That is not something that is achieved immediately or when we suddenly find we need it. It is something that we should seek out and enable so that when the special time of challenge comes we already have a network or at least a few others who know us and love us sufficiently to be able to come alongside and hopefully help heal us if the burdens have proved too great. The Apostle Paul lists his prayer partners at the end of his letter to the Colossian Christians. These were relationships that went deeper than being the recipients of an emailed prayer letter.

Even before reading John Stott's allusion to the *guru-shishya* model of spiritual leadership, I wondered how much this model had unconsciously crept into attitudes of mission leadership in India. In recent years my wife and I have been privileged to give hospitality to some younger Indian scholars and teachers. Some of them have shared how they have been humbled and challenged by the occasional teacher or leader who has been open and self-giving with them as postgraduate students or junior leaders in a team, even to the point of vulnerability. What we are talking about here is the ability to love and be loved even where lines of authority and leadership would seem to make this difficult.

William Carey clearly went through a period of feeling alone, bereft, isolated and abandoned. This came to a head, calling into question his own sense of God's call that had been challenged by his wife's increasing mental disturbance and his own awareness that his gifts were not in preaching. The coming of Ward and Marshman six years after Carey landed in India, with their skills in typesetting and printing, enabled him to embark upon what became his lasting life work, translating the Bible into many Indian languages. Carey's own failure to recognise and trust the warnings and test the judgement of others was repaired by the realisation of his own misunderstanding of what his gifts and calling truly were, and by the arrival of colleagues from whom nothing was hidden and to whom his vulnerability and the suffering of his family were only too apparent.

No leader possesses all the gifts, and in some cases the very genius of the person may obscure the flaws in their personality. Such people have been used by God throughout history for their creativity and vision. Strategies must be taken, however, to surround them with people of strength so that together they may form an effective team. As John Stott states in his book *Calling Christian Leaders,* the model we have from Christ is of humility before a congregation or whatever body of Christians we are called to lead, to love and to serve. That will include learning to trust others enough to be loved. Many of the casualties in Christian service are people who have sought to be humble and love those committed to their leadership, but had not learned how to be humble enough, love enough and to be loved in turn by those other members of the body to whom they belong.

Chapter Seventeen
THE MISSIONARY CALL

For several years I thought the Lord was calling me to be a missionary, and then in 1954 I developed tuberculous meningitis, which meant many months in hospital and even after recovery, an uncertain future health-wise, making it unlikely that I would be able to go overseas. My question for 20 years was: 'Why, Lord?'

This is the background to my consideration of the topic of the missionary call, which I shall look at through the lens of my desire to serve overseas, my reading of scripture and my experiences in medicine and psychiatry.

Christian workers have special problems in this area. It is not that they are more likely to break down than their secular colleagues, nor do they have more psychological problems. In fact, they do better than other expatriates. They have a lower return rate from overseas. The children of missionaries may have problems but often they cope extremely well. Missionary marriages do break up but a far higher number survive.

We do well to remember that the highest spiritual work often produces the greatest conflicts. Entry into Satan's strongholds and spiritual battles means a high level of engagement, and some Christian workers may have great difficulty in seeing the strategies that Satan uses. They may not realise when they need special counselling or medical, including psychiatric, help. Other Christian workers may be able to help but a return to the home country may be necessary. Some of those who suffer from depression can accept help, but some missionaries may refuse treatment, putting it all down to Satanic attacks.

The psychological aspects of missionary life

Our call

What do we mean by our call? 35 to 50 percent of missionaries come home early or do not return to the mission field after the first term. Many factors are involved in this including health, politics, the local church, pressure from parents or the children's education. This inevitably raises the question as to whether their initial guidance was wrong. Some hard questions follow and there is often a sense of failure and grief. These hard questions need to be asked right from the start when seeking guidance, before departure as well as when serving abroad. For example, how much is this work needed for personal reasons or for family reasons? What is the job doing for us at a personal level? Do we need to be needed as part of our own personal affirmation? We are called to service but do we expect gratitude from those we serve? We are doing spiritual work but is that the same thing as the assurance of God's will for us? Does that make us first-class Christians with the evidence of total commitment for God? Are we going because we enjoy exotic travel or because we lack prestige in our community back home? We may go to avoid difficult parents. We may go to avoid competition in career structures at home. We may go to repeat the family heritage of missionary activity of parents and grandparents. We may go because we have no roots elsewhere. Many of these reasons are not wrong in themselves, but what if parents back home become ill? What if we find it difficult to be subservient to the nationals? What if we are not accepted? If we have not already faced up to these questions then these problems may be brought to the fore. This often makes us fight against the mission or against God.

It is clear that we all have mixed motives and many immature and un-thought-through motives may draw us. Many of us are adolescents, by which I mean 25 or younger, when we feel the call to mission service and may be inspired by a particular biography or speaker. But both of these sources may give us edited accounts and often we do not have the maturity and experience to evaluate them properly.

None of this negates the call and indeed the love of travel, the absence of roots, the need to be needed and the idea of service may well confirm or help our call or conviction. But if there is a residual component unacknowledged, unnoticed or denied, then we are vulnerable on those occasions when our work comes under pressure or when we are personally faced with conflict. The more subjective, inward or personal our motivation is, and the more associated with other life events our call is, the more open we are in all our ministries to stress, difficulties and disappointment. We may well feel convinced of the call of God and others may have confirmed that call. These personal factors do not invalidate it, but they need to be looked at and discussed with a trusted friend.

We have the powerful example of Jesus and his disciples. Each of them came with mixed motivations and Jesus knew it. They had good reasons and bad reasons for following him but Jesus still worked with them. This did not affect the reality of their call but it did affect how Jesus had to deal with them before and after his death.

Our expectations
What expectations do we have of missionary work? How do we expect God to work through us? What do we feel is our special gift? The person who is very sure of their special gifts needs the assessment of others.

Often we spend much time trying to find our gifts, but we will never know what they are until we start serving God by serving others, so we should keep our eyes and heart open to see who needs help. My first task in a new church was to tidy the pews between services. Scripture is full of people who felt their gifts lay elsewhere than proved to be the case: Moses did not know where his gifts lay and had to be shown; Elijah thought he did but then considered himself a failure as Jezebel still lived and he had not eliminated Baal worship. That task was left to Elisha and a pagan king. The Apostle John ended up on the small island of Patmos alone but wrote Revelation.

Marjorie Foyle was a gynaecologist who went out as a missionary to Nepal but ended up closing down hospitals and thought herself a failure. She retrained in psychiatry to minister to missionaries on the field and had a second career of great importance to countless Christian workers

Our call and our work is to serve the Lord with the gifts he has given us and those that others see in us. He may have several careers in store for us. And the more we are attached to our call, our gifts, our work, the more painful may God's dealings with this have to be. Not many missionary biographies are as honest as the Bible writing about Elijah. I have written elsewhere about W C Burns who had a remarkable influence on Hudson Taylor though his own missionary work in China showed little fruit during his lifetime. His biography moved me more than any other as a student, but it was not a success story.

Our personality

How does our personality affect our work? Marjorie Foyle says that it is one of the major factors leading to stress on the mission field. There is nothing new in this. Look at the disciples and how their personalities developed. Impetuous Peter learned gradually to react less violently. His brother, Andrew, by contrast was pragmatic and matter-of-fact. Paul was a pioneer. He needed his colleagues but was a bit rough with them sometimes. By contrast Barnabas was a facilitator and encourager who went to look for Saul and encouraged him having seen the grace of God working in him. Without him humanly speaking Paul may not have become a great missionary and church statesman. We need more people like Barnabas who will raise up Pauls and also pick up the young John Marks whom Paul impatiently left behind.

We see the same in church history down the centuries. Wesley was loving and gracious but had great difficulty with women. John Sung was an abrasive, driven depressive and caused great friction with his colleagues. By comparison Watchman Nee was a gracious man who was a third-generation Christian. All of us are imperfect, with flaws. That does not mean God cannot use us but we need to discern, to recognise, to reflect, to modify.

Missionary boards are often not good at picking up those personality differences that will cause problems. Special problems may not be disclosed or discussed and if there is lack of candour, there may be no learning from experience until it is too late. Moreover, some personality issues may be manageable in the home setting but not in another culture. This is very important because personality differences may be hidden, unrecognised, or coped with previously, but under stress, isolation or provocation can erupt and can escape control. Anxiety may lead to panic. Fussiness can lead to scrupulousness. Irritability can lead to destructive aggression. Half of those needing psychiatric care on the mission field have shown some symptoms before they arrived there.

Special events like bereavements, a change of job or a change of base, difficult relationships with colleagues or one's spouse, or specific illnesses can all lead to problems. This is much more apparent in a place of relative isolation or a different culture and the admission of needing help may be thought of as a failure and unspiritual.

There are certain behaviours indicative of insecurity and immaturity. First, rigid authoritarianism can cause havoc among colleagues, especially where the person rushes into conflict. The rigid person is insecure and immature, like a child who wants things kept exactly the same as before. Authoritarianism has no openness to others and cannot see the positive side in the approaches of others. In the Christian setting the person may say, 'I prayed over it and God has spoken to me.' This has a forcefulness that is not wrong of itself but it is good sometimes to admit that one can be mistaken and be open to listening to others.

For the perfectionist on the other hand, there is a meticulousness that brings havoc to oneself and causes conflict for others. It is 'all or nothing' and the standard is high. This person is not prepared to make mistakes or learn by trial and error. There is the fear of failure rather than the desire to succeed.

There is the need of certainty rather than accepting risk. There is conflict avoidance rather than loss of face. There is the need for approval, perhaps an absent father's approval, and this person is often critical of others.

There are particular problems in certain groups of people. Pastors' wives often have a hard time, as does the only child of older parents, or children from a highly educated father who makes big demands on his children. Both in the church and on the mission field these people may have poor self-esteem, and Christian service may be a way of compensation. They may be drawn to the least attractive situation to prove their worth. Then they give 110 percent to the work as any less will be counted as failure. This leads to exhaustion and to depression for they have no reserves. This in turn can lead to uncertainty and then to paralysis. They cannot risk conflict and are terrified to be proved wrong or lose control, so they despair and become depressed.

So what is the solution? The treatment is the fellowship of others and learning and being helped by the fellowship to a sober assessment of oneself as Paul describes in Romans 12. It is biblical to make mistakes, that is how one matures. The danger is if these aspects of our behaviour are not recognised and the person blames others for their difficulties, they may feel at loggerheads with the mission society, or their colleagues or the new arrivals on the mission field. They may feel unappreciated, put upon or taken for granted, and before long a hardness enters into their soul, which may lead to a chronic festering sore and depression engulfs. Such was the case with George Muller and John Nelson Darby who were never able to make up their differences, to the great loss of the renewal in which they were involved. But if one is prepared to recognise the signs and symptoms, to listen to friends and the church fellowship, it is possible to change and to mature. Ask what would be positive, ask how to pace oneself in this situation. Learn to value others and this will lead to the building up of the church.

Chapter Eighteen
Psychological Aspects
in Missionary Relationships

Under this heading there are four areas of relationship that I would like to consider:

Colleagues

According to a survey of several thousand missionaries, three quarters of problems that missionaries face are related to their colleagues. The disciples were no different. They had squabbles over 'Who is the greatest?' Teamwork was not their greatest skill. The same was true of the church's early missionary work: Paul, Barnabas, Peter and Demas all had issues with their colleagues. Paul couldn't even visit Corinth because it was too painful, he just wrote rather sharp letters. I doubt if any Christian anywhere can avoid interpersonal differences. My wife would say that on the days when I see patients I come home tired but relaxed, but when I am involved in committee meetings I'm wound up and need to talk about it.

There is an unrealistic attitude among many Christians here. Perhaps we need to pay heed to this little ditty:

Oh to dwell with saints above, that will be true glory. But to dwell with saints below, that's another story!

We all bring our differences and difficulties into our relationships with colleagues, along with our personality or background or culture. We are often aware of the differences and less often of the strengths in others, especially when we are under pressure.

As Christians we are involved in a common enterprise, yet missionaries are often individualists. In Roman Catholic missions the concept of a team may be much greater. The Jesuits or Franciscans, for example, are committed to an 'order', which is not the same as a mission or a church organisation.

I have experience of working in two teams where tensions arose because of interpersonal differences, first in the clinical team in hospital and second in the church leadership team. Regular meetings are essential with sufficient time to thrash out issues. Open confrontation may occur. There must be a preparedness to challenge and be challenged but each person must be valued. Many Christians are afraid of confrontation, which may lead to frustration in others. One colleague avoided me for 15 years. Later on we met and he remarked, 'We agree on far more than I expected.' He probably could not risk even then expressing disagreement.

Some workers who struggle with authority are still working out complex relationships, perhaps with their own fathers, and for me the greatest difficulty arose when certain junior staff made me a 'father figure'. They might be searching for the perfect father in a leader or an older colleague. They will always be disappointed for perfection is not to be found on this side of eternity. The letter to the Hebrews speaks rather of 'stirring one another up to love and good works' and 'encouraging one another' (Hebrews 10:24-5).

Singleness

Aloneness is not the same as loneliness. Some of the loneliest people I know are married. The mission field is the worst place to go for the single woman hoping to marry or looking for a husband. It's not the best place for a single man looking for a woman either, because the situation is so abnormal and home leave often only exaggerates the differences.

There has been a preponderance of single women on the mission field, often in positions of authority. Some of the most impressive and able figures have been women, for example Mary

Slessor, Amy Carmichael, Mother Theresa. But it is noticeable how often they have been in caring roles. Sometimes there has been conflict about their role in leadership or administration but many have had to take on these roles.

The single person needs their own home and space every bit as much as do couples. They need privacy and a place where they can entertain and stamp their own identity. Shared accommodation should be the exception not the rule. On furlough they need apartments or a place to stay and it should not be automatically assumed that they are just going back to their parents. I believe there should be special attempts to give as much respect and dignity to the single person, whether male or female, as to married couples. This world has little or no concept of singleness and as Christians we have a witness here too to give dignity to the celibate.

We should help to stimulate relationships among single people. Married couples have the possibility of an exclusive one-to-one relationship, which they take around with them. Single people do not have that but there are many other different relationships that they can have, preferably with both sexes and in groups. This can allow them to commit themselves to people. It is often more difficult in the missionary situation and cross-cultural problems also need to be taken into account. We express our sexuality in many different ways, not just genitally. Men are often dominant and competitive. Women often see needs, can give reassurance and many are very creative, reflecting God's creative nature.

It is often said that the single person is free to move, is more mobile and has less 'baggage', but I suggest this is as much a question of temperament as of state. The married person takes their supportive structures around with them, whereas if the single man or woman moves they will have to create and find new structures. They will have to set up home; they will have to make friends; they will have to make their own entry into a new environment.

Spouses

Paul wrote to Timothy to remind him that the church leader must maintain his own household well, otherwise how can he care for God's household. Yet isolation, depression and marital tensions occur in many wives of pastors and Christian workers. One Christian director of an international mission said to me, 'Ministers' wives get a raw deal from their husbands and missionaries' wives get an even worse deal from theirs.' It is most often the wife who bears the brunt of things. It is she who is depressed, despairing and ostensibly the problem. While this is not limited to missionaries and can affect all marriages, there are aspects particular to the missionary situation. Here the couple have left behind all their friends and the support structures that surrounded them and are cast more and more upon each other.

So what are the factors that cause problems within these marriages? First, communication differences and the giving and receiving of love, which is not necessarily the same thing. Communicating the feeling of being loved and supported must result in the other partner feeling loved. Some people have enormous differences in the way they show affection. The husband may say, 'You know I love you or I wouldn't do this or that.' But the woman may ask, 'What am I to you? What difference do I make to you?' Jesus speaking to Peter said, 'Do you love me?' 'Yes,' said Peter, 'of course you know I do', but he had a lot to learn about how to show it.

I sometimes ask couples to look at each other and then tell me why they married that person. I won't accept the answer 'because I loved them'. What first brought them to your attention? One person confessed to me many years after he was married that it was his wife's legs that attracted him to her!

The missionary wife, especially with children in an isolated place or having had to leave children at home, needs all the more the affirmation of being loved and appreciated. Her ministry and gifts may have to be put into cold storage. Marjorie Foyle commented that God has an enormous freezer ready for this purpose! Difficult as this may be in the missionary situation, some couples need to take time to open up in communication, take a weekend away together each year, have someone look after the kids and do the same for others later. Ask each other: 'What would you like me to do for you?' Something that is practical, repeatable and mutually acceptable.

William Carey's wife Dorothy, and David Livingstone's wife, Mary, were deeply affected by the hardships of life. This is well recounted in 'Wives of Fame' by Edna Healey, where she tells the story of Mary Livingstone, Emma Darwin and Jenny Marx. There's a curious trio for you! There may be a great cost in being a 'Wife of Fame'.

The situation may be compounded by the fact that they are 'doing the Lord's work', for how can a wife criticise this work that they are doing together? Then there is the guilt and the envy of others, frustration leading to anger, leading to yet more guilt. Overarching all is the feeling that she cannot argue with God. So she accepts physical, intellectual and spiritual isolation as she accepts relative poverty and her husband's absences. The Apostle Peter, himself a married man, has a special word for couples in I Peter 3:7, which husbands especially would do well to take to heart.

Children
All this has a direct relevance to children. If they see their mother depressed, that leads to insecurity. 'Am I to blame; why can't we make mother happy?' They may not see Father as a father but only as a mission official. These children may be searching for a father, for someone they can trust. This is especially a problem for sons who feel they cannot measure up to their fathers. When they were young and had physical tussles, Father always won, but later on with emotional tussles Father cannot always win. Children need to be able to say the things they feel. Yes, it may hurt, but if they are unable to experience that, they may be more worried or afraid and think the worst of themselves.

Missionaries' children, like psychiatrists' children, live lives very publicly, in a goldfish bowl, under scrutiny and invoke natural curiosity. They need to be assured of our interest, concern, presence and understanding.

We are all far from perfect. We all have different backgrounds. We need time to discuss, to allow discussion, dissension and restoration. Missionaries on furlough need uninterrupted holidays with their children. They need to share a common interest, or if there is no common interest they need to show an interest in the children's interests, which may be easier at some stages of life.

Third culture children are not raised in their parents' home country, and are not native to the country in which they live. This is true of the children of diplomats, the Armed Forces, businesspeople as well as missionaries. Few of these children are rebels. They learn early what is acceptable and understand their parents' ministry. They are like orchids – they take their roots with them. They are fascinating children – they can be moved but they need tender care. The average missionary child at 18 has lived in eight places. They are good at hiding their emotions and they don't open up easily. They are interested in learning languages, are used to hearing different sounds and 90 percent are bilingual as adults. Almost 100 percent want to return to what they call 'home'.

Often they are good judges of character, observant and wary. One quarter of US missionary kids end up in the diplomatic corps in the Far East. On the surface they may be quiet and often don't go for big groups, but inwardly are creative and express ideas on paper. Many come to life in the host culture. They sing, play the guitar, have foreign friends. Most have a desire for service and 80 percent will do international work. They are used to change, they like change, are opportunists, high achievers, but may be older – in mid to late 20s – before they settle into a career.

Going back to their parents' country needs preparation. They think of it as a foreign country and will have to learn the rules. They often find it difficult to know how to talk to peers or what to talk about. If brought up elsewhere, even settling back for a period may never give roots in the parents' country. It may be too late as already they are third culture people. One third marry other third culture people, 20 percent marry cross-culturally but the success is equivalent to other marriages. Settling back is occasionally difficult, especially given the US and UK's growing animosity to foreigners at home and abroad. However, the majority of missionary kids regard theirs as a positive experience and feel positive towards their parents.

Chapter Nineteen
CULTURE SHOCK AND COUNTER-CULTURE SHOCK

Culture shock is the mixture of feelings that follows an abrupt change of environment, classically when an individual moves from one country to another. This event causes the discontinuity of social relationships that have been previously relied on for the maintenance of self-esteem, relationships that have frequently been taken for granted.

It is akin to a bereavement reaction in that it is a response to loss and as in a bereavement reaction there are complicated emotions. There may be self-blame: 'I made a mistake and got it wrong.' They may blame society for not giving warning, blame the church for not being helpful and blame God for allowing it to happen. As in every bereavement the first six months are usually the worst and then one slowly adapts to the job of living again.

Culture shock has been part of the migrant experience over many generations: the loss of security, the loss of family and friends and the loss of cultural clues. In the latter case an example would be learning how to hear the word 'no' being said without it being verbalised directly. Many misunderstandings have been caused when the directness of one culture has collided with the politeness of another. Loss of verbal skills and misunderstanding can lead to a feeling of helplessness.

I would add that missionaries traditionally do well in this area. Many have a desire to adapt to the culture, to learn the language and to communicate well for a specific task. But the feeling that this is for real and for the long haul can still be perturbing. Mistakes made by the missionaries may be thought of as failures and can mean that they think they are not settled and have mistaken God's call.

All may seem to be going well and then homesickness strikes, rather like the unexpected waves of emotion after a bereavement described by C S Lewis in *A Grief Observed*. Even when the worst is over, maybe after six months, there are still adjustments in coming to terms with the situation and moving on, and as in the bereavement situation this may happen over one or two years. The first Christmas, the first Easter, the first winter or summer is always difficult. The second year one knows what to expect. Because loss, distress, readjustment, tiredness and questioning are all part of the adjustment, it is essential to go through these in some measure, otherwise the missionary never engages in a deep way in their new life and culture.

Mistakes are often made and a properly constructed orientation beforehand could help to avoid mistakes. Conflict in the new situation occurs for a number of reasons:

a) Money is often a huge issue. There may be poverty around in the local culture, but if the missionary lives in poverty they become inefficient as a worker. Often the only white people known are Christians, therefore if you're a Christian you may automatically be thought of as wealthy. This may be a particular issue with those working in famine relief.

b) The missionary may think they have been sent to do 'spiritual work', but administration is often necessary and consumes time and energy. There may be the feeling that the missionary society didn't spell this aspect out properly.

c) The host society may often be very family-orientated and struggle to understand the single missionary or the one who has come without their family, when for them the family comes first.

d) Professional standards may be a problem. The missionary has come to help and to instruct but may be expected to pass those who would fail at home, to do without safety checks, or to cope with that which classes as inefficiency at home. This may lead to critical attitudes and the missionary becoming fretful and either wanting to give up or getting angry.

Migration and mental illness are often associated

There are three categories of migrants abroad. In the first category the *gastarbiter* or guest worker goes to earn, not to learn, and returns home. In the missionary context he goes at the invitation of the national churches, is temporary, but while there expects and is expected to integrate. In the second category the settler has a positive design to integrate and to assimilate. He has a strong motivation to identify with the culture, the language and the way of life. It is a voluntary calling to identify, albeit incompletely, with the way of life and often dress of the people to whom they go. In the third category is the exile, the involuntary migrant who may have the most severe emotional problems and chronic disorders.

In the past, the missionary was like the third: they went into enemy territory for the Lord's sake and many died and never returned home. Nowadays the missionary situation is in some ways more complex, a variant of all three, and this complexity has potential for conflict and stress.

There are a number of ways in which the situation may be helped, if the missionary can:

a) Make friends with several of the nationals but not ask too much of them.

b) Be what they are. It is one's basic attitude that will eventually win through; if you love the people to whom you are ministering the recipients will feel it. It may take time to communicate, but it is consistency that counts in any language and in any culture.

c) Develop a special interest in the new environment and culture. One missionary in China took an interest in Chinese porcelain and bronze; another working in India became an expert in Himalayan ascents and flora; Dr John Stott inspired many missionaries to enjoy the variety of God's creation, especially ornithology. 'Consider the birds', he used to say, quoting our Lord in Matthew's Gospel. He invariably included a day of bird-watching in his overseas tours.

d) Keep links with home. Acknowledge the ambiguity of one's situation and be regular in responding to messages from home, taking full advantage of the range of electronic possibilities where there is electricity available.

Reverse culture shock

Reverse culture shock or re-entry stress can happen on home assignment or on retirement. These days with air travel there is little time to adjust between the two worlds. There may be confusion with the sense of a detached unreality compounded by fatigue and lack of motivation. It is a well-known mental mechanism, when feelings have not caught up with facts.

In retirement it is as if the 'bereavement' process occurs again but this time one is older and less able to change. There is no longer the sense of anticipation, and there may be the feeling that one's life's work is done. Family and friends may be scattered, and instead of leading, one becomes a nobody, anonymous in the supermarket rather than being known in the bazaar. One's roots may be dried out, with a feeling of coming to an alien soil after a rich sojourn abroad.

Any retirement needs preparation, and re-entry from missionary life requires even more care and planning. There is often great disappointment and anxiety. One is expected to be happy and excited at the prospect of coming home, when in fact everything is strange, as though one has been in a time capsule.

Majorie Foyle in her book *Honourably Wounded* speaks of battle-scarred missionaries. But some wounds only become apparent after retirement, especially if following long and faithful service and where the returning missionary has not kept up with friends or trends. Mission boards should have a central role in this area and also churches when they have been the main sending agency, as is often the case nowadays.

Chapter Twenty
THE ROLE OF MISSION BOARDS
AND SENDING CHURCHES

L et us consider the role of mission boards in relation to home assignment. Care needs to be taken of missionaries on furlough, which should be carefully planned beforehand. Correspondence should be clear and precise. If information needs to go to medical personnel in the home country for health screening on return, then a copy of that letter should be sent to the missionary, to show that the communication is open. Nothing breeds suspicion and frustration more than lost or secret communication.

On arrival the missionary should be met. There should be a place to go and unpack baggage and not only baggage but also worries and frustrations. There should be a person to whom the missionary can talk, and talk, and talk! Perhaps over a meal or out for a walk but not in an office. Housing should be available and churches may help in this by purchasing or renting a flat or a house. A holiday as soon as possible is essential: two weeks is no good, three weeks is good, a month is ideal. For the families this allows consolidation and gives time for refreshment and recuperation not only for parents but also for their children who may get disorientated if overexposed to a plethora of new people.

Then comes the time to embark on visits, deputation and proper debriefing. Some missionaries dread deputation work, others enjoy it. Speaking as a consumer, some missionaries are not good speakers, others are enjoyable and full of information. I have always watched with detachment exhausted missionaries, entertainer missionaries, dishonest missionaries (not that that was deliberate but important bits were left out) and real communicators. Why not release the real communicators to meet the key churches and release the tired missionaries and the poor communicators to visit their specific centres and churches.

Might it be possible to encourage people from key churches to use their holidays to visit missionaries in the field? This would need to be sensitively handled, so that the visitor is aware of cultural pitfalls that could cause offence and compromise the missionary's relationship with the local community. But it would allow the visitors to do the deputation work back at home where they are known and respected and hopefully know how and with whom to communicate. I have known churches that have done that and it has caught the imagination of the whole church, not just the missionary-minded.

Pastoral care by mission boards

How aware is the mission board of the conditions of service? What kind of person cracks? A keen person may be too earnest, too compulsive, too perfectionist, making too heavy weather of life. A person with low self-esteem and high levels of anxiety may lack energy, may be preoccupied with physical health. The personality of the missionary needs to be spotted, not necessarily that they should be rejected but that they need to be sent to a suitable place. Personal history and family history is important and may predispose to things going wrong. If somebody is wounded in service it is the mission board's responsibility thereafter. It will not do to say that 'it's the Lord's service and it's the Lord's responsibility'.

Communication is a recurrent theme. As an observer, I think the battle for souls is a bit like the Battle of the Somme in 1916 when the war office decisions were made by men with no battle experience and no real experience of trench warfare. The officers and the men in the trenches had to charge to their deaths on orders that bore no relation to reality. It may not be quite like that in the missionary situation but again that has been my impression of some missionary boards. I was once made aware of three outstanding missionaries who felt reduced to soldiers in the trenches; they were given orders that affected the family and their children's schooling with no consultation and no redress. There was an explanation given, but as orders came from on high there was no discussion. On another occasion a mission board sent a circular to all its mission partners asking them to please avoid being robbed, or being involved in a traffic accident as this was causing the mission high insurance costs! There was no mention of any concern for the safety or well-being of the missionaries.

The most heartrending cases I have had to deal with are the missionaries who had no one to pastor them. This is often because they couldn't or wouldn't trust anyone local. Sometimes they believed those who could help wouldn't. If that is our attitude where there are national leaders, then we should beware of paternalism at best and racism at worst. We should pray about this and we should be on the lookout. Missionaries should be encouraged first and foremost to find local Christians to pray with and share with and to be accountable to.

I often hear the phrase, 'it is the Lord personally who is our sufficiency', but part of that sufficiency needs to be supplied by the body of Christ wherever that is, as in Hebrews 10:24 where the instruction is not to neglect to meet together, to stir one another up and to encourage each other. If we are in a situation where that is not possible locally, then we should look for our Tychicus (Colossians 4:7), who knew all about Paul's situation, or our Onesimus, who visited Paul from the Colossian church. When Paul was hurt and rejected by Demas he was ministered to by Tychicus and Onesimus. Sometimes the support of the Onesimus from the sending church may be needed until the missionary has built up a depth of friendship and trust with the local national leaders. Who is sufficient? Let us be prepared to learn that God has given us more than sometimes we are ready to receive.

This book was produced by

www.wordsbydesign.co.uk

Words by Design offers a range of services to
individual and corporate clients, as well as to the
printing and publishing industry.

In a digital age, authors wish to publish their own
books; families seek to research and write the history
of their ancestors; businesses see the marketing
significance of commissioning their corporate history;
and publishers use freelance experts in all the many
varied stages of publishing.

At Words by Design we have the necessary experience
and knowledge to help with these and many other
projects. With expertise in research, writing, editing,
design, photography, typesetting and print
production, we aim to be able to help on any project.

office@wordsbydesign.co.uk
+44 (0)1869 327548